W9-BGM-857

DAYBOOK

OF CRITICAL READING AND WRITING

daybook, *n.* a book in which the events of the day are recorded; *specif.* a journal or diary

THE AUTHORS
* Fran Claggett
* Louann Reid
* Ruth Vinz

Great Source Education Group
A division of Houghton Mifflin Company
Wilmington, Massachusetts

THE AUTHORS

✶ **Fran Claggett**, an educational consultant, writer, and teacher at Sonoma State University, taught high school and college English for more than thirty years. Her books include *Drawing Your Own Conclusions: Graphic Strategies for Reading, Writing, and Thinking* (1992) with Joan Brown, *A Measure of Success* (1996), and *Teaching Writing: Art, Craft, and Genre* (2005) with Joan Brown, Nancy Patterson, and Louann Reid.

✶ **Louann Reid** taught junior and senior high school English for nineteen years and currently teaches courses for future English teachers at Colorado State University. She has edited *English Journal* and is the author or editor of several books and articles, including *Learning the Landscape* and *Recasting the Text* (1996) with Fran Claggett and Ruth Vinz. She is a frequent consultant and workshop presenter nationally and internationally.

✶ **Ruth Vinz with Cammie Lin.** Ruth taught in secondary schools for twenty-three years and is currently a professor of English education at Teachers College, Columbia University. She is author of numerous books and articles that focus on teaching and learning in the English classroom. Cammie Lin, currently a doctoral student at Teachers College, taught middle and high school in New York City for many years.

REVIEWERS

Randolph C. Bernard
Lafayette, Louisiana

James Desmond
Commack, New York

Susan Dinges
Budd Lake, New Jersey

Dr. Tim Hart
Urbana, Ohio

Harriet Maher
Lafayette, Louisiana

Brook E. Meiller
Norman, Oklahoma

Marie Raduazzo
Arlington, Massachusetts

Elizabeth Rehberger
Huntington Beach, California

Sean R. Ruday
Boyce, Virginia

Tracy A. Scholz
Houston, Texas

Rebecca McKinlay Sheinberg
Houston, Texas

EDITORIAL: Barbara Levadi and Sue Paro
DESIGN AND PRODUCTION: AARTPACK, Inc., and Richard Spencer

Contents

Focus/Skill		Selection/Author	

Focus/Skill		Selection/Author	

Investigating Texts

In this *Daybook* you will use **five essential strategies** of reading and writing to practice different methods of **inquiry**. Here are the **five essential strategies** of reading and writing:

- Interacting with the text
- Making connections
- Exploring multiple perspectives
- Focusing on language and craft
- Studying an author

These strategies are powerful tools to help you engage in *inquiry* as you read and write. If you were asked to *inquire* into your city's curfew laws, what does that mean? You might read articles and news accounts, interview city officials and police officers. You might solicit opinions from your peers and their parents. As you inquire, you look at details, ask questions, and form opinions. It also means that you keep your mind open to all possible answers, opinions, and solutions.

In this unit, you will inquire into how memory and imagination work together to give writers ideas for the texts they write. You will examine your own writing and think about how your experiences, knowledge, and imagination influence you as a reader and writer.

INTERACTING WITH THE TEXT

Imagine that your best friend is telling you about something that just happened. In order to understand what is important to her, you do more than just sit there. You interact with her as she tells her story. You listen, focus on particular points, or ask for clarification. Reading is similar. When you interact with a text, you pay close attention. **Interacting with the text** helps you collect information, ask questions, and clarify understandings.

A good way to keep track of your interactions with a text is to **read with your pen.** As you read, you can use your pen to

- circle words you don't know or understand;
- underline important phrases, repetition, or key images;
- make notes near confusing parts;
- ask questions and record reactions;
- make comments like "I wonder . . . ," "What if. . . ?" and "That makes me think about . . . "

In the *Daybook*, use the **Response Notes** column to carry on a conversation with the text, or read with your pen. Notice how one reader interacted with the text. Add your own comments to the one already there.

Roadside Caesarean Saves a Fawn by Chris Smith

Response Notes

David Koester is a roofer, not an obstetrician, but he kneeled at the side of a highway near Guernville a few days ago and performed a extraordinary delivery.

The new arrival has big, big ears but it's truly a little deer.

"I just marvel . . . that he had the presence of mind to do that," said Marge Davis, who is bottle-feeding this particular fawn and six others as a volunteer with the Sonoma Wildlife Rehabilitation Center.

"He did a beautiful job," she said.

The impromptu midwife said this is what happened:

He and his fiancée, Allison McCracken, were taking a drive after supper Wednesday and just before dusk were approaching Guerneville on Highway 116.

Koester was rounding a curve, he said, when a doe "came ripping down the bank and into the front of my truck. I'd slowed down quite a bit but I didn't stop, and I hit her."

Koester pulled off the highway and ran to the doe, but as a lifelong hunter familiar with wildlife he knew at once the animal was dead. He saw also that it was pregnant—and then he saw its belly jiggle.

I wonder how he knew how to do that!?

"I reached down and felt the shin of a front leg of a young one still kicking and moving inside," he said. With his dull, old pocket knife he then opened up the dead deer and out dropped a male fawn.

✳ When you interact with a text, pause to collect your thoughts. Pause now to think about what you have read. Record words and phrases that reflect your thoughts and questions.

_____

_____

_____

_____

Continue reading the article, using your pen to make notes.

Leaving the doe, Koester asked his fiancée to drive and he held the fawn in his lap on the way back to Healdsburg. He said the strong, little animal kicked and tried to stand all the way home.

Within two hours of its birth, the fawn was standing. Wednesday night it slept on the floor beside Koester's bed.

But the next day, Thursday, Koester asked McCracken to call around and see if any organization accepts such young wild animals.

She found the Wildlife Rehabilitation Center, which really owns no center but has about 40 Sonoma County volunteers willing to care for animals in their homes.

The organization put Koester and McCracken in touch with Davis, who already had six fawns and some baby raccoons at her ranch south of Kenwood. She told them to come on over Thursday evening.

Delivery man Koester said he was glad to put his fawn in capable hands, but he confessed it wasn't easy letting the wide-eyed little animal go.

"It tore me up," he said. "Allison and I had a good cry." ❖

✳ Another way to interact is to have a conversation with others.

■ Compare your **Response Notes** with a partner's notes. Record any new thoughts.

■ What are the different ways you interacted with this text?

_____

_____

_____

_____

✳ Imagine that you are having a conversation with Koester after he experienced this event. If you could talk with him, what might you ask and say? How do you think he might respond? Record both sides of the conversation here.

_____

_____

_____

_____

_____

_____

_____

_____

_____

_____

✳ Interact with the text by imagining that you are Koester. Write a journal entry in which you reflect on the experience.

What were the most helpful ways for you to interact with the news article, and why do you think they were helpful?

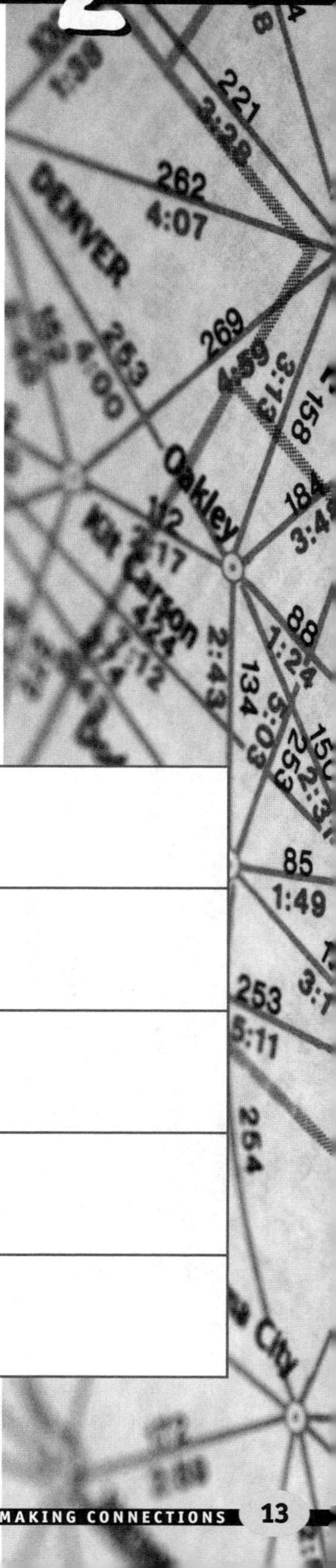

The topics authors choose to write about often connect with their memories of personal experiences. Some writers stick closely to those experiences, while others take the basic idea and imagine something new. Writers use their ideas and shape them into news articles, essays, poems, stories, plays, or films so that you can make your own connections.

Engaged readers **make connections** between the text and their own experiences, other texts, and the world around them. Describe the strongest connection you made with the article you read in Lesson 1. How did connecting with the text help make the story come alive for you?

_____

_____

_____

_____

Connect with the story by taking Koester's point of view. Take time to recreate the moment described in the article. What do you imagine he saw, heard, or felt? Reread the article, "Roadside Caesarean Saves a Fawn." Concentrate on which of your senses are activated.

Fill in the Sensory Chart below, as if you were there with Koester.

What could you SEE?	
What could you HEAR?	
What could you SMELL?	
What could you physically FEEL?	
What emotions could you FEEL?	

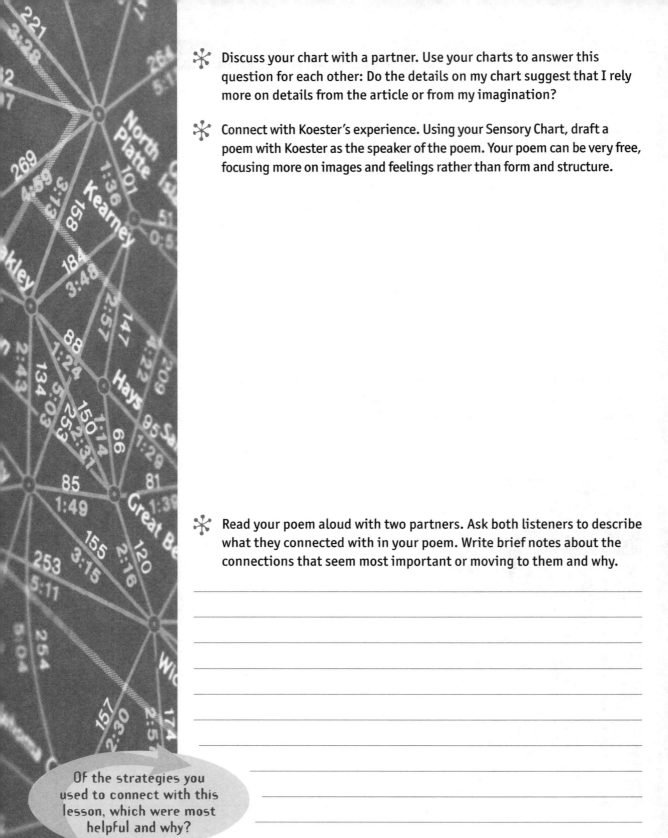

✳ Discuss your chart with a partner. Use your charts to answer this question for each other: Do the details on my chart suggest that I rely more on details from the article or from my imagination?

✳ Connect with Koester's experience. Using your Sensory Chart, draft a poem with Koester as the speaker of the poem. Your poem can be very free, focusing more on images and feelings rather than form and structure.

✳ Read your poem aloud with two partners. Ask both listeners to describe what they connected with in your poem. Write brief notes about the connections that seem most important or moving to them and why.

_____

_____

_____

_____

_____

_____

Of the strategies you used to connect with this lesson, which were most helpful and why?

_____

_____

_____

Think about this statement for a moment: *Poetry does not have to be factual to be true.* What do you think this means? Free-write about it for a few minutes. Then compare your response with a partner's.

_____

_____

_____

_____

One way to think about the statement is to consider to what degree memory and imagination are based on truth. Much depends on the perspective from which events or feelings are shared. For example, a poem may convey the emotions a person felt or the internal struggle he or she experienced at a particular moment. The connection that a writer has to an event will determine the writer's perspective. That perspective often guides the writer in selecting what gets told. **Exploring multiple perspectives** helps you take a close look at the different **points of view** and lenses that create the writer's experience.

When you read the following poem, imagine that the narrator is a driver facing a situation similar to Koester's. As you read, you will see that the story takes a different turn. Record your reactions and thoughts in your **Response Notes.**

Traveling Through the Dark by William Stafford

Traveling through the dark I found a deer
dead on the edge of the Wilson River Road.
It is usually best to roll them into the canyon:
that road is narrow; to swerve might make more dead.

By glow of the tail light I stumbled back of the car
and stood by the heap, a doe, a recent killing;
she had stiffened already, almost cold.
I dragged her off; she was large in the belly.

My fingers touching her side brought me the reason—
her side was warm; her fawn lay there waiting,
Alive, still, never to be born.
Beside that mountain road I hesitated.

Response Notes

I wonder what killed this deer.

The car aimed ahead its lowered parking lights;
under the hood purred the steady engine.
I stood in the glare of the warm exhaust turning red;
around our group I could hear the wilderness listen.

I thought hard for us all—my only swerving—
then pushed her over the edge into the river. ❖

✳ In a few sentences describe your reactions to and questions about the poem.

_____

_____

_____

_____

_____

✳ Explain why you think the two drivers made different choices. Discuss your reasons with a partner. Record your best ideas here.

_____

_____

_____

_____

✳ Write a parallel poem by telling a story of your own where you had to make choices. Tell the story as if you were describing what happened to a friend. Present the situation and the choices. To help you create your poem, follow the steps outlined on pages 16–18.

1 Describe a time when you had to make a difficult decision.

_____

_____

_____

_____

_____

_____

What could you SEE?	
What could you HEAR?	
What could you SMELL?	
What could you physically FEEL?	
What emotions could you FEEL?	

List two possible choices you had, and note the possible outcome for each of the choices.

Choice One	Possible Outcome
Choice Two	**Possible Outcome**

4 Write the story line of your poem in a few brief sentences.

_____

_____

_____

_____

_____

_____

_____

_____

_____

5 Decide which choice you will explore in your poem. It could be a choice you really made, or it could be an alternative. Think about what happened or would happen as a result of your choice. (This will become the reflective part of your poem.) Describe it here.

_____

_____

_____

_____

_____

_____

_____

_____

6 Explain your choice. Does your perspective, or point of view, influence your choice? How?

_____

_____

_____

_____

_____

_____

_____

✳ Use your notes to draft your poem.

Title _____

✳ Share your poem with a partner. Read it aloud. Then have your partner read it aloud to you. After sharing, point out elements in your poem that are your memories of what really happened and identify other elements that reveal your true feelings and values.

How does seeing multiple perspectives enrich your understanding of an experience?

FOCUSING ON LANGUAGE AND CRAFT

Think about a time when you made a great effort to tell a story that conveyed an important or difficult experience. Chances are, you chose your language carefully. When poets tell stories, they select their language to evoke a response in readers or listeners. Consider this statement by William Stafford: "A poem is anything said in such a way or put on the page in such a way as to invite from the hearer or reader a certain kind of attention." When you are **focusing on language and craft**, you pay attention to the poet's word choice as well as how poets use their words to evoke a certain kind of attention, or response.

Use the chart below to analyze and compare how you and Stafford use language and craft to tell your stories. You may need to reread your poem and Stafford's as you complete the chart.

Language and Craft	William Stafford's poem, "Traveling Through the Dark"	Your poem, "_____"
Describe the vocabulary used. Which words may evoke a strong response in readers or listeners?	*Words are simple and spare—"stood by the heap"*	
List sensory words that create visual pictures that make the reader "hear" something or feel a certain emotion.	*"glow of the tail light"*	
What is the tone the poet uses (for example, serious, sad, sarcastic, funny)? Describe and give examples.		
How does the poem use language in a way that invites readers to find out what happens? Explain.		

✳ Use the chart to help you write how Stafford's use of language and
craft evokes a response in you as a reader.

_____

_____

_____

_____

_____

_____

_____

✳ Reread and revise your poem, focusing on how you use language and
craft to evoke a powerful response from readers. Write the revised
poem below.

Title _____

✳ Read your revised poem aloud to a partner, and then
discuss the response it evokes in him or her.

What did you learn about
language and craft from Stafford
that will be useful to you in your
own writing?

When you read a piece of literature, you interact with it in a way that allows you to create meaning. Your own experiences and perspective inform the meaning that you find through reading the text. It is not necessary to know about the author's life for you to find a story or poem meaningful. However, inquiring about an author's life experiences and perspective can add another dimension to your reading.

Read the following selection, written by William Stafford. As you read, pay particular attention to connections you can make between Stafford's experiences with nature and the poem, "Traveling Through the Dark." Record your thoughts in your **Response Notes**.

Response Notes

Are conscientious objectors usually in tune with nature?

Views on the Writer's Vocation
from *Writing the Australian Crawl* by William Stafford

Our family is from Kansas, the middle of it, where I was born. We moved from one little town to another during my school years, following my father's jobs, which varied, but always provided income for our needs and books. We liked the towns and countryside, where we fished, hunted, and camped along the mild, wandering streams. Our lives were quiet and the land was very steady. Our teachers were good. Not till I finished my BA degree at the University of Kansas and went on to graduate school in another state did I ever see an adult drunk or enraged or seriously menacing. Higher education and the coming of World War II supplied a new aspect of experience.

As a pacifist I was in camps for <u>conscientious objectors</u> from 1940 till 1944. We <u>fought forest fires, built trails and roads, terraced</u> eroding land, etc. . . .

✳ Compare your **Response Notes** with a partner's. Describe the strongest connection you made between the writer, this part of his biography, and the poem, "Traveling Through the Dark."

_____

_____

_____

_____

_____

_____

_____

✳ Imagine you have the opportunity to ask William Stafford anything you want about his poem, "Traveling Through the Dark." What are you curious about? What would you like to know about his experiences or perspective that might inform your reading of the poem? Write your questions here.

_____

_____

_____

_____

_____

Sometimes we hear directly from authors commenting on their work, whether in talks, interviews, or essays. In this case, you are going to read an excerpt from a personal letter Stafford wrote to a friend and fellow poet, Ted Kooser. In this letter Stafford describes how he imagines the driver of the car in "Traveling Through the Dark." As you read, write **Response Notes** about how this letter informs, or changes, the way you read the poem.

Letter to Ted Kooser by William Stafford

About my poem "Traveling Through the Dark," my own feeling (though I'm ready for anyone to fish out their own any time) is that the speaker is alone in the car, and that when he says "our group" he is saying two things, the immediate one being just whatever is suddenly preciously there—deer, fawn, car, engine, exhaust—whatever can hurriedly be clustered together by someone feeling abruptly scarily alone. The other part of a meaning, or shade of a meaning I feel is that the speaker feels a kind of representative, suddenly, for all those others who must depend on isolated individuals carrying out their obligations even when alone—so that our group hears the wilderness listen any time we become aware of how alone we sentient beings are in a world with cliffs, rocks, death around. . . . ✜

Adios—
Bill Stafford

What is a person's responsibility?

✳ Discuss your **Response Notes** with a partner. Add any new thoughts.

❋ Stafford describes the speaker who feels like "a kind of representative" and indicates that the decision to push the deer over the edge may be for the protection of others. Think about a time when you were a "kind of representative" for other people and you had to make a decision that would affect others, even if they were not there. Fill in the graphic below with your reflections about the incident.

Describe the situation and whom you "represented."	What were your choices?	What did you decide to do and why?

❋ Use your graphic to write about the incident. Share your draft with a partner.

Title _____

How does knowing about Stafford and relating his reflections to your own help you to understand and connect with his poem?

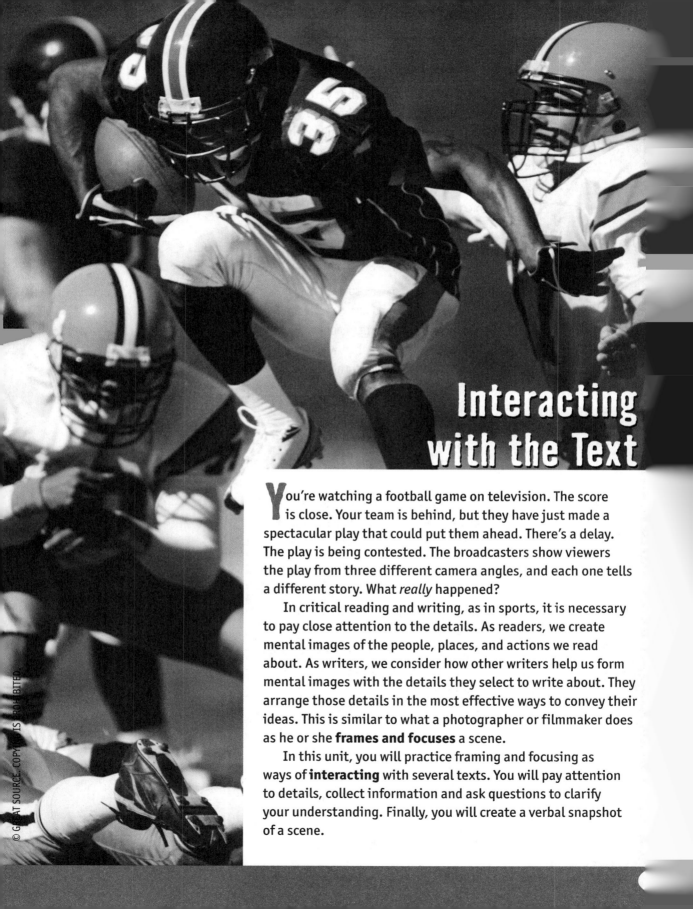

Interacting with the Text

You're watching a football game on television. The score is close. Your team is behind, but they have just made a spectacular play that could put them ahead. There's a delay. The play is being contested. The broadcasters show viewers the play from three different camera angles, and each one tells a different story. What *really* happened?

In critical reading and writing, as in sports, it is necessary to pay close attention to the details. As readers, we create mental images of the people, places, and actions we read about. As writers, we consider how other writers help us form mental images with the details they select to write about. They arrange those details in the most effective ways to convey their ideas. This is similar to what a photographer or filmmaker does as he or she **frames and focuses** a scene.

In this unit, you will practice framing and focusing as ways of **interacting** with several texts. You will pay attention to details, collect information and ask questions to clarify your understanding. Finally, you will create a verbal snapshot of a scene.

Fully understanding what you read requires **close attention** to the **details** in the text. When you view a scene or read a description, your brain forms an immediate impression about what is in front of your eyes. An image or scene becomes more specific the longer you look.

Doodling is a way to tap into your visual images. Read or listen to "The Last Wolf." In the **Response Notes**, draw pictures or symbols that come to you.

The Last Wolf by Mary TallMountain

the last wolf hurried toward me
through the ruined city
and I heard his baying echoes
down the steep smashed warrens
of Montgomery Street and past
the few ruby-crowned highrises
left standing
their lighted elevators useless
passing the flicking red and green
of traffic signals
baying his way eastward
in the mystery of his wild loping gait
closer the sounds in the deadly night
through clutter and rubble of quiet blocks

I heard his voice ascending the hill
and at last his low whine as he came
floor by empty floor to the room
where I sat
in my narrow bed looking west, waiting
I heard him snuffle at the door and
I watched
he trotted across the floor

he laid his long gray muzzle
on the spare white spread
and his eyes burned yellow
his small dotted eyebrows quivered

Yes, I said.
I know what they have done. ❖

Response Notes

✳ Look at your doodling. What details from the poem have you emphasized? Mark those details with a highlighter or by underlining them.

✳ Re-examine the poem to answer this question: How does Mary TallMountain use the poem to comment on the growth of cities and how that growth affects the environment? Write a letter to someone who has not read the poem, explaining what you think is TallMountain's comment. Tell whether you agree or disagree. Quote words from the poem to show your reader what you mean.

Dear _____ :

_____

_____

_____

_____

_____

_____

_____

_____

_____

_____

_____

_____

_____

_____

_____

_____

_____

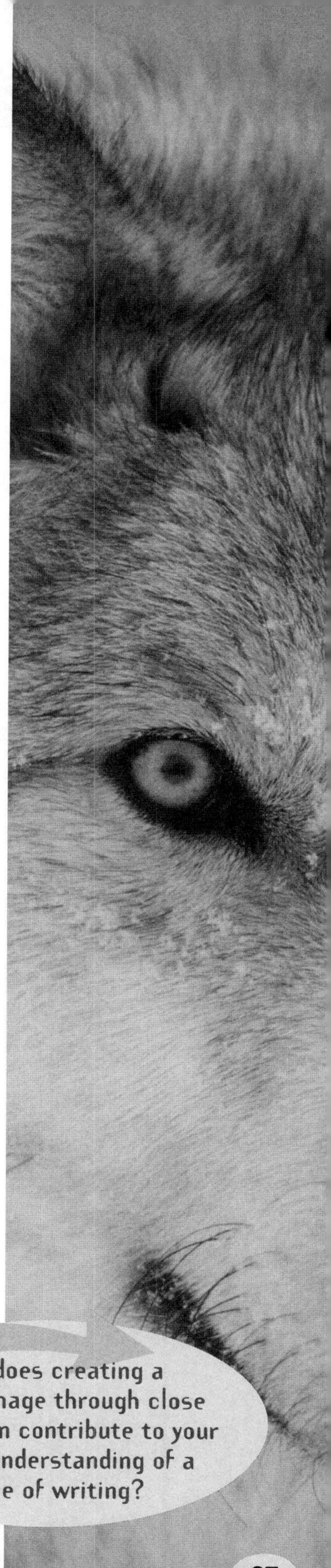

How does creating a mental image through close observation contribute to your overall understanding of a piece of writing?

Sincerely,

SELECTING DETAILS

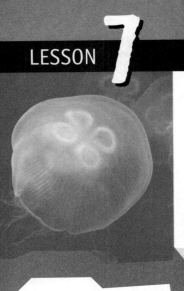

As readers, we want enough detail in the text so that we can actually envision a scene. We want the author to select the most significant **details** and arrange them in such a way that we can **visualize** the text.

Notice the details that Ernie Pyle, a news correspondent, has included in this excerpt from an essay about Allied forces landing on the beach at Normandy (France) during World War II. Circle the details that help you to visualize this scene. Use the **Response Notes** to ask questions about what you're reading.

Response Notes

What's the purpose of a good-luck symbol among all the death and destruction?

from **Brave Men** by Ernie Pyle

I took a walk along the historic coast of Normandy in the country of France. It was a lovely day for strolling along the seashore. Men were sleeping on the sand, some of them sleeping forever. Men were floating in the water, but they didn't know they were in the water, for they were dead.

The water was full of squishy little jellyfish about the size of a man's hand. Millions of them. In the center of each of them was a green design exactly like a four-leafed clover. The good-luck emblem. Sure. Hell, yes.

I walked for a mile and a half along the water's edge of our many-miled invasion beach. I walked slowly, for the detail on that beach was infinite.

The wreckage was vast and startling. The awful waste and destruction of war, even aside from the loss of human life, has always been one of its outstanding features to those who are in it. Anything and everything is expendable. And we did expend on our beachhead in Normandy during those first few hours.

For a mile out from the beach there were scores of tanks and trucks and boats that were not visible, for they were at the bottom of the water swamped by overloading, or hit by shells, or sunk by mines. Most of their crews were lost.

There were trucks tipped half over and swamped, partly sunken barges, and the angled-up corners of jeeps, and small landing craft half submerged. And at low tide you could still see those vicious six-pronged iron snares that helped snag and wreck them.

On the beach itself, high and dry, were all kinds of wrecked vehicles. There were tanks that had only just made the beach before being knocked out. There were jeeps that had burned to a dull gray. There were big derricks on caterpillar treads that didn't quite make it. There were halftracks carrying office equipment that had been made into a shambles by a single shell hit, their interiors still holding the useless equipage of smashed typewriters, telephones, office files.

There were LCTs turned completely upside down, and lying on their backs, and how they got that way I don't know. There were boats stacked on top of each other, their sides caved in, their suspension doors knocked off.

In this shore-line museum of carnage there were abandoned rolls of barbed wire and smashed bulldozers and big stacks of thrown-away life belts and piles of shells still waiting to be moved. In the water floated empty life rafts and soldiers' packs and ration boxes, and mysterious oranges. On the beach lay snarled rolls of telephone wire and big rolls of steel matting and stacks of broken, rusting rifles.

On the beach lay, expended, sufficient men and mechanism for a small war. They were gone forever now. And yet we could afford it.

We could afford it because we were on, we had our toehold, and behind us there were such enormous replacements for this wreckage on the beach that you could hardly conceive of the sum total. Men and equipment were flowing from England in such a gigantic stream that it made the waste on the beachhead seem like nothing at all, really nothing at all.

But there was another and more human litter. It extended in a thin little line, just like a high-water mark, for miles along the beach. This was the strewn personal gear, gear that would never be needed again by those who fought and died to give us our entrance into Europe.

There in a jumbled row for mile on miles were soldiers' packs. There were socks and shoe polish, sewing kits, diaries, Bibles, hand grenades. There were the latest letters from home, with the address on each one neatly razored out— one of the security precautions enforced before the boys embarked.

There were toothbrushes and razors, and snapshots of families back home staring up at you from the sand. There were pocketbooks, metal mirrors, extra trousers, and bloody, abandoned shoes. There were broken-handled shovels, and portable radios smashed almost beyond recognition, and mine detectors twisted and ruined.

There were torn pistol belts and canvas water buckets, first-aid kits, and jumbled heaps of life belts. I picked up a pocket Bible with a soldier's name in it, and put it in my jacket. I carried it half a mile or so and then put it back down on the beach. I don't know why I picked it up, or why I put it down again.

Soldiers carry strange things ashore with them. In every invasion there is at least one soldier hitting the beach at H-hour with a banjo slung over his shoulder. The most ironic piece of equipment marking our beach—this beach first of despair, then of victory—was a tennis racket that some soldier had brought along. It lay lonesomely on the sand, clamped in its press, not a string broken.

Two of the most dominant items in the beach refuse were cigarettes and writing paper. Each soldier was issued a carton of cigarettes just before he started. That day those cartons by the thousands, water-soaked and spilled out, marked the line of our first savage blow.

Writing paper and air-mail envelopes came second. The boys had intended to do a lot of writing in France. The letters now forever incapable of being written that might have filled those blank abandoned pages.

Always there are dogs in every invasion. There was a dog still on the beach, still pitifully looking for his masters.

He stayed at the water's edge, near a boat that lay twisted and half sunk at the waterline. He barked appealingly to every soldier who approached, trotted eagerly along with him for a few feet, and then, sensing himself unwanted in all the haste, he would run back to wait in vain for his own people at his own empty boat. ... ❖

✳ **What is your initial impression of this scene? Why?**

_____

_____

_____

_____

_____

_____

Ernie Pyle arrived on the beach at Normandy the morning after the forces landed. His close observation of the area resulted in a massive catalog of items. He directs the reader's attention to the importance of the various objects he sees. For example, he stresses the human loss of the invasion when he turns his attention to the "strewn personal gear, gear that would never be needed again by those who fought and died to give us our entrance into Europe." Mark examples of similar commentary in the essay.

✳ Use a three-column chart to examine Pyle's selection and arrangement of details. In the left column, list the details you circled as you read and any others you now want to include. In the middle column, tell how these details made you feel or the impression they left on you. In the right column, tell what importance Pyle gives the items.

Detail	Impression	Importance
Diaries	It makes me sad to think that personal stories are ended this way.	"Those who fought and died" don't need their diaries anymore.

How do authors emphasize their ideas by the ways they select and arrange details?

FRAMING THE SCENE

In the excerpt from *Brave Men* (pages 28–30), Pyle has created a **verbal snapshot,** a written description of a place or a moment in time. Within it are several scenes, arranged in order from a big picture of the ocean and the invasion beach to a close-up of the dog and the empty boat. Read the excerpt again to remind yourself of how he has arranged details for the greatest impact.

✳ Select one part of the text to draw. Highlight the details in the text. Use the author's language to guide your illustration. Your artistic ability is not important; the emphasis is on your observation of the details.

❋ Another way to study the arrangement of details in an excerpt is to imagine that you are going to film it. Discuss with a partner how you would film this scene. When would you have the camera show the whole area in a wide-angle shot, and when would the camera take a close-up? What effects would these decisions have on the viewer? With a partner, make a story board for this excerpt. A **story board** is a series of panels that show rough sketches of key scenes. Select the six most important elements that will create an action sequence. You can also add sound effects and dialogue to your drawings.

1.

2.

3.

4.

6.

5.

How did you decide what to include and what to exclude for each frame in your story board?

Have you ever felt that what you have read is fuzzy or out of focus? One way to focus your reading is to ask questions. **Clarifying questions** should lead to answers that either reveal something that you did not know or confirm something you suspected but were not sure of. They should make your mental image sharper. They should also help you focus on the details that are particularly important.

Read "Mnemonic" by Li-Young Lee at least twice, recording your questions in the **Response Notes.**

Response Notes

Mnemonic by Li-Young Lee

I was tired. So I lay down.
My lids grew heavy. So I slept.
Slender memory, stay with me.

I was cold once. So my father took off his blue sweater.
He wrapped me in it, and I never gave it back.
It is the sweater he wore to America,
this one, which I've grown into, whose sleeves are too long,
whose elbows have thinned, who outlives its rightful owner.
Flamboyant blue in daylight, poor blue by daylight,
it is black in the folds.

A serious man who devised complex systems of numbers and rhymes
to aid him in remembering, a man who forgot nothing, my father
would be ashamed of me.
Not because I'm forgetful,
but because there is no order
to my memory, a heap
of details, uncatalogued, illogical.
For instance:
God was lonely. So he made me.
My father loved me. So he spanked me.
It hurt him to do so. He did it daily.

The earth is flat. Those who fall off don't return.
The earth is round. All things reveal themselves to men only gradually.

I won't last. Memory is sweet.
Even when it's painful, memory is sweet.

Once, I was cold. So my father took off his blue sweater. ❖

Would Father's memories always have a logic and an order?

✳ What is your initial impression of this poem?

_____

One way to come up with effective questions is to use four steps to clarify information. Then ask questions for each step. In the space after each step, write a question about "Mnemonic."

1 **Collect** information—for example, who is the speaker, what is the situation, or subject?

_____

_____

_____

_____

_____

2 **Connect** the information you have into patterns or categories, seeing how the pieces of information are related.

_____

_____

_____

_____

_____

3 **Construct** statements or inferences about the relationships you found among the bits of information.

_____

_____

_____

_____

4 **Draw conclusions** about the meanings of the text. Decide which conclusions are supported by the information and inferences.

_____

_____

What additional questions might you ask to clarify your understanding of what you read?

CREATING A VERBAL SNAPSHOT

You have read from the poetry and essay genres in this unit. You have also used several tools to inquire into how writers select and arrange details that will support a comment they want to make or an opinion they want to express. To interact with the text, you have

- Doodled and observed your drawings to connect them to details in a poem
- Circled details that helped you to visualize
- Drawn the images that selected words helped you to visualize
- Created a story board of the six most important parts of a scene
- Asked questions to clarify information

✳ You will use some of these tools to write a verbal snapshot in which you use an object, scene, person, or animal to comment on a topic important to you. Use the following boxes to collect ideas.

Topic	Audience	Genre
global warming	peers	letter to the editor of the school paper

DEVELOP YOUR TOPIC

How will you develop your topic? Will you use a striking contrast, as Mary TallMountain ("The Last Wolf") did? Will you use a single object and related ideas, as Li-Young Lee ("Mnemonic") did? Or will you describe a scene, as Ernie Pyle (*Brave Men*) did?

✳ Discuss your ideas with a partner to decide which ones are the most promising. Jot down one or two that you could work with. Draft a statement of the opinion you might want to express about each topic. Then choose one topic and complete the following chart:

Connections to you	Audience	Genre	Opinion	Possible details and means of development (contrast, object, scene, etc.)
I love polar bears.	peers	letter to the editor	Global warming must be stopped	A lone polar bear on an ice flue

SELECT AND ARRANGE DETAILS

✳ Imagine that you are looking at a photograph of the object, scene, person, or animal that you will describe. Draw or write down everything you see.

_____

_____

_____

_____

_____

_____

_____

DRAFT YOUR SNAPSHOT

✳ Use your notes on pages 36–37 to draft your verbal snapshot.

Which technique best helped you create a verbal snapshot of your topic, and why was that technique the best way to communicate to your reader?

Making Connections

Good stories entertain us, scare us, teach us, make us laugh, make us cry, and make us think. Some of the best stories do all of these. Think about a story you read that stayed with you long after you read it. What effect did it have on you? Why do you think it had such an effect? Often the stories that stay with us the longest are those with which we make the most **connections**. We may connect those stories to stories in other books or movies, of people we know, or from our own lives.

In this unit you will read several **memoirs**, true accounts that are reflections of the authors' lives. You will explore the ways in which these authors construct their memoirs, and you will practice making connections with them by

- connecting through memories;
- monitoring the sources of your connections;
- making text-to-text connections;
- connecting multiple stories;
- connecting through writing.

You will ask: What connections do I make with these memoirs, and how do these connections help me to better understand my own and the writer's experiences?

CONNECTING THROUGH MEMORIES

Memoirs are stories in which writers reflect on their life experiences. In such stories, writers recall memorable moments, trips, accidents, first loves, family stories. Whatever the subject matter, memoirs have one thing in common—the story is told in the **first-person point of view**, using *I*. Memoirs are, however, not a record of a person's life experiences. If writers recorded *every* experience in their lives, no matter how small or big, they would write memoirs several thousand pages long! Instead, they choose events, sometimes seemingly minor, but sometimes major, to illustrate experiences that have affected who they are and how they see the world.

Consider this question as you read the following excerpt from Isabel Allende's autobiographical work, *Paula*: How do writers choose which memories to write about? Use **Response Notes** to note your reactions and any connections you make to the text.

Response Notes

The writer creates a feeling of darkness and heaviness.

from **Paula** by Isabel Allende

I place one hand over my heart, close my eyes, and concentrate. There is something dark inside. At first it is like the night air, transparent shadow, but soon it is transformed into impenetrable lead. I try to lie calmly and accept the blackness that fills my inner being as I am assaulted by images from the past. I see myself before a large mirror. I take one step backward, another, and with each step decades are erased and I grow smaller, until the glass returns the reflection of a seven-year-old girl. Me.

It has been raining for several days; I am leaping over puddles, my leather bag bouncing against my back. I am wearing a blue coat that is too large for me and a felt hat pulled down to my ears; my shoes are sodden. The huge wooden entry door, swollen by rain, is stuck; it takes all my weight to pull it open. In the garden of my grandfather's house is a gigantic poplar with roots growing above the ground, a scrawny sentinel standing guard over property that appears abandoned—shutters hanging from their hinges, paint peeling from walls. Outdoors it is just getting dark, but inside it is already deepest night. All the lights are off except in the kitchen. I walk through the garage toward the light. The walls of the cavernous kitchen are spotted with grease, and large blackened saucepans and spoons hang from iron hooks. One or two fly-specked light bulbs cast a dull light on the scene. Something is bubbling in a pot and the kettle is whistling; the room smells of onion, and an enormous refrigerator purrs in a corner. Margara, a large woman, with strong Indian features and a thin braid wound around her head, is listening to a serial on the radio. My brothers are sitting at the table with cups of hot cocoa and buttered bread. Margara does not look up. "Go see your mother, she's in bed again," she scolds. I take off my coat and hat. "Don't strew your things about; I'm not your slave, I don't have to pick up after you." She turns up the volume on the radio. I leave the kitchen and confront the darkness in the rest of the house. I feel for the light switch and a pale glow barely fills the hall with its several doors. A claw-footed table holds the marble bust of a pensive girl; there is a mirror with a heavy wood frame, but I don't look because the Devil might be reflected in it. I shiver as I climb the stairs; currents of air swirl through an incomprehensible hole in the strange architecture. Clinging to the handrail, I reach the second floor. The climb seems interminable. I am aware of silence and shadows. I walk to the closed door at the end of the hall and tiptoe in without knocking. A stove furnishes the only illumination; the ceilings are covered with the accumulation of years of paraffin soot. There are two beds, a bunk, a sofa, tables and chairs—it is all I can do to make my way through the furniture. My mother, with Pelvina López-Pun asleep at her feet, is lying beneath a mountain of covers, her face half-hidden on the pillow: straight nose, high cheekbones, pallid skin, finely drawn eyebrows above closed eyes. "Is it you?" A small, cold hand reaches out for mine.

"Does it hurt a lot, Mama?"

"My head is bursting."

"I'll go get you a glass of warm milk and tell my brothers not to make any noise."

"Don't leave. Stay here with me. Put your hand on my forehead, that helps."

...I'm hungry, I want to go down to the kitchen and drink my cocoa, but I must not leave my mother, and besides, I don't have the courage to face Margara. My shoes are wet and my feet feel like ice. I stroke my mother's poor head and concentrate: everything depends on me now. If I don't move, and pray hard, I can make the pain go away. ❖

✳ Write a word that accurately describes the strongest impression, image, or reaction you had while reading about this incident. Write how that word helps to explain what you find most interesting in Allende's story. Tell what effect the story has on you.

_____

_____

_____

_____

✳ Share with others what you have written. Discuss what you think Allende is trying to say about herself in this scene. Record your best ideas below.

_____

_____

_____

Allende said, "I take one step backward, another, and with each step decades are erased and I grow smaller, until the glass returns the reflection of a seven-year-old girl." Allende's memoir can help you think about some of the experiences that have most influenced who you are today. Reflect on those experiences in order to practice **connecting through memories**. Begin thinking about memoirs you can write from your own life. To help you "step backward" in time, create a Memory Catalog of your meaningful experiences. Include important moments or events from your life that you think might be interesting topics for your writing.

✳ List topics under each of the headings in the chart below. Include words, phrases, or names that will remind you of specific experiences. Space is provided for you to create additional headings of your own.

MEMORY CATALOG

A time I felt happy	A time I felt scared	A time I felt proud	A time I felt upset
An experience that taught me about myself			

How does a memoir serve as a way to reflect on life for both the writer and the reader?

When you are engaged with a story, you make connections to it. If you pay attention to what is happening in your mind as you read or hear the story, you will probably notice that your memories and thoughts about the story help you to make sense of it. In other words, you make connections with memories from your own life and from other stories you have read, heard, or seen.

Making connections is an important part of reading. Sometimes the connections come easily, but other times it can be difficult to make them. In this lesson you are going to keep track of the connections that you make to the story. As you read the following excerpt from a memoir by Zora Neale Hurston, record the connections in your **Response Notes**.

from **I Get Born** by Zora Neale Hurston

Response Notes

This is all hear-say. Maybe, some of the details of my birth as told me might be a little inaccurate, but it is pretty well established that I really did get born.

The saying goes like this. My mother's time had come and my father was not there. Being a carpenter, successful enough to have other helpers on some jobs, he was away often on building business as well as preaching. It seems that my father was away from home for months this time. I have never been told why. But I did hear that he threatened to cut his throat when he got the news. It seems that one daughter was all that he figured he could stand. My sister, Sarah, was his favorite child, but that one girl was enough. Plenty more sons, but no more girl babies to wear out shoes and bring in nothing. I don't think he ever got over the trick he felt that I played on him by getting born a girl, and while he was off from home at that. A little of my sugar used to sweeten his coffee right now. That is a Negro way of saying his patience was short with me. Let me change a few words with him—and I am of the word-changing kind—and he was ready to change ends. Still and all, I looked more like him than any child in the house.

Of course, by the time I got born, it was too late to make any suggestions, so the old man had to put up with me. He was nice about it in a way. He didn't tie me in a sack and drop me in the lake, as he probably felt like doing.

People were digging sweet potatoes, and then it was hog-killing time. Not at our house, but it was going on in general over the country, like, being January and a bit cool. Most people were either butchering for themselves, or off helping other folks do their butchering, which was almost just as good. It was a gay time. A big pot of hasslits cooking with plenty of seasoning, lean slabs of fresh-killed pork frying for the helpers to refresh themselves after the work is done. Over and above being neighborly and giving aid, there is the food, the drinks and the fun of getting together.

So there was no grown folks close around when Mama's water broke. She sent one of the smaller children to fetch Aunt Judy, the mid-wife, but she was gone to Woodbridge, a mile and a half away, to eat at a hog-killing. The child was told to go over there and tell Aunt Judy to come. But nature, being indifferent to human arrangements, was impatient. My mother had to make it alone. She was too weak after I rushed out to do anything for herself, so she just was lying there, sick in the body, and worried in mind, wondering what would become of her, as well as me. She was so weak, she couldn't even reach down to where I was. She had one consolation. She knew I wasn't dead, because I was crying strong.

Help came from where she never would have thought to look for it. A white man of many acres and things, who knew the family well, had butchered the day before. Knowing that Papa was not at home, and that consequently there would be no fresh meat in our house, he decided to drive the five miles and bring a half of a shoat, sweet potatoes, and other garden stuff along. He was there a few minutes after I was born. Seeing the front door standing open, he came on in, and hollered, "Hello, there! Call your dogs!" That is the regular way to call in the country because nearly everybody who has anything to watch, has biting dogs.

Nobody answered, but he claimed later that he heard me spreading my lungs all over Orange County, so he shoved the door open and bolted on into the house.

He followed the noise and then he saw how things were, and being the kind of man he was, he took out his Barlow Knife and cut the navel cord, then he did the best he could about other things. When the mid-wife, locally known as a granny, arrived about an hour later, there was a fire in the stove and plenty of hot water on. I had been sponged off in some sort of a way, and Mama was holding me in her arms.

As soon as the old woman got there, the white man unloaded what he had brought, and drove off cussing about some blankety-blank people never being where you could put your hands on them when they were needed.

He got no thanks from Aunt Judy. She grumbled for years about it. She complained that the cord had not been cut just right, and the belly-band had not been put on tight enough. She was mighty scared I was going to have a weak back, and that I would have trouble holding my water until I reached puberty. I did.

The next day or so a Mrs. Neale, a friend of Mama's came in and reminded her that she had promised to let her name the baby in case it was a girl. She had picked up a name somewhere which she thought was very pretty.

My mother says I screamed real loud, too, when I was born.

Perhaps, she had read it somewhere, or somebody back in those woods was smoking Turkish cigarettes. So I became Zora Neale Hurston.

There is nothing to make you like other human beings so much as doing things for them. Therefore, the man who grannied me was back next day to see how I was coming along. Maybe it was pride in his own handiwork, and his resourcefulness in a pinch, that made him want to see it through. ❖

✳ Share your **Response Notes** with a partner. Help each other decide which of your connections stands out, or is the strongest. Describe it below.

_____

_____

✳ Review your **Response Notes** to see how many connections you made to your own life, how many you made to other texts, and how many you made to other stories you have heard. Which kind of connection did you make the most? List at least three.

_____

_____

_____

✳ Zora Neale Hurston writes, "This is all hear-say. Maybe, some of the details of my birth as told me might be a little inaccurate, but it is pretty well established that I really did get born." Obviously, this story does not come from an actual memory. Hurston constructs the memory from what she has heard from others about the day of her birth. Try to make a connection to memoir writing by thinking about stories from your own life that you may not really remember but have heard from others. List them below.

_____

_____

_____

_____

_____

How has your understanding of a memoir changed as a result of reading Hurston's memoir?

MAKING TEXT-TO-TEXT CONNECTIONS

In Lesson 12 you listed "memories" you couldn't actually remember, but ones you could construct into stories based on details you have learned. What were some of the ways you learned these details? When did you learn them?

The following excerpts are from a **memoir** titled *Black, White, and Jewish: Autobiography of a Shifting Self.* The author, Rebecca Walker, is the daughter of a famous writer with whom you may be familiar, Alice Walker. Notice the way she weaves her "memories" into stories about her birth and first birthday. As you read, **monitor the connections** you make. Pay particular attention to the connections you make to yourself and to other texts, such as those you read in Lessons 11 and 12. Record your connections in your **Response Notes.**

Response Notes

from Black, White, and Jewish: *Autobiography of a Shifting Self* by Rebecca Walker

You may want to ask about the story of your birth, and I mean down to the tiniest details. Were you born during the biggest snowstorm your town had seen in fifty years? Did your father stop at the liquor store on the way to the hospital? Did you refuse to appear, holding on to the inside of your mother's womb for days? Some sinewy thread of meaning is in there somewhere, putting a new spin on the now utterly simplistic nature-nurture debate. Your job is to listen carefully and let your imagination reconstruct the narrative, pausing on hot spots like hands over a Ouija board.

I was born in November 1969, in Jackson, Mississippi, seventeen months after Dr. King was shot. When my mother went into labor my father was in New Orleans arguing a case on behalf of black people who didn't have street-lights or sewage systems in their neighborhoods. Daddy told the judge that his wife was in labor, turned the case over to co-counsel, and caught the last plane back to Jackson.

When I picture him, I conjure a civil rights Superman flying through a snowstorm in gray polyester pants and a white shirt, a dirty beige suede Wallabee touching down on the curb outside our house in the first black middle-class subdivision in Jackson. He bounds to the door, gallantly gathers up my very pregnant mother who has been waiting, resplendent in her African muumuu, and whisks her to the newly desegregated hospital. For this final leg, he drives a huge, hopelessly American Oldsmobile Toronado.

Mama remembers long lines of waiting black women at this hospital, screaming in the hallways, each encased in her own private hell. Daddy remembers that I was born with my eyes open, that I smiled when I saw him, a look of recognition piercing the air between us like lightning.

And then, on my twenty-fifth birthday, Daddy remembers something I've not heard before: A nurse walks into Mama's room, my birth certificate in hand. At first glance, all of the information seems straightforward enough: mother, father, address, and so on. But next to boxes labeled "Mother's Race" and "Father's Race," which read Negro and Caucasian, there is a curious note tucked into the margin. "Correct?" it says. "Correct?" a faceless questioner wants to know. Is this union, this marriage, and especially this offspring, correct?

✳ Making connections from one text to another is one way to deepen your understanding. Compare and contrast this story to the one you read in Lesson 12. Take a moment to reread both selections if it's helpful.

"Black, White and Jewish"	Shared	"I Get Born"

Now read another excerpt from the same memoir. Record your connections, thoughts, and reactions as you read.

On my first birthday I am given my favorite foods: chitterlings and chocolate cake. Daddy goes to Estelle's, the soul food place on the other side of town where he is the only white customer, and brings me home a large order of the pig intestines. Mama puts me in my big wooden high chair with the smooth curved piping, and then feeds me one slimy pale gray glob after another while Daddy sits at the table, grinning.

After I have eaten all of the chitterlings, Mama has to peel my tiny fingers from the container to make me let it go. Then she sets a chocolate cake with a big number one candle sticking up from the middle down in front of me, singing "Happy Birthday" softly, so that only I can hear. For a few seconds Mama and Daddy wait, expectant and wide-eyed, to see what I'll do. I giggle, squeal, look at them, and then dig into the cake with my bare hands, smearing the sticky sweetness all over my face and pushing what's left into my mouth. I rub cake in my hair, over my eyes. I slap my hands on the high chair, putting some cake on it, too.

My parents laugh out loud for a few seconds; then my father wraps his arm around my mother's waist, patting her hip with a cupped hand. For a few seconds we are frozen in time. Then my father pushes his chair out from the table, cuts himself a piece of the chocolate cake, and goes to work. ❖

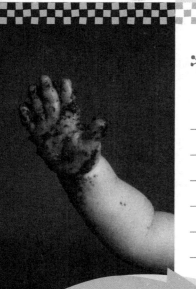

✳ In Lesson 12 you listed stories of your own—those you can't literally remember but that you could construct from what you have learned in other ways. Describe one of these memories.

_____

_____

_____

_____

_____

_____

_____

_____

How does examining other writers' ways of creating memoirs help you to write your own?

In her collection of memoirs and essays, *In Search of Our Mothers' Gardens,* Alice Walker tells the story of an "accident" that greatly affected her life. Like Allende's story in Lesson 11, Walker was just a young girl at the time of the memory, yet she recounts the incident with great detail. As you read, pay particular attention to the **connections** you make between this story, the other memoirs in this unit, and your own memories. Record them in the **Response Notes.**

from **In Search of Our Mothers' Gardens** by Alice Walker

It was great fun being cute. But then, one day, it ended.

I am eight years old and a tomboy. I have a cowboy hat, cowboy boots, checkered shirt and pants, all red. My playmates are my brothers, two and four years older than I. ...my parents decide to buy my brothers guns. These are not "real" guns. They shoot "BBs," copper pellets my brothers say will kill birds. Because I am a girl, I do not get a gun. Instantly I am relegated to the position of Indian. Now there appears a great distance between us. They shoot and shoot at everything with their new guns. I try to keep up with my bow and arrows.

One day while I am standing on top of our makeshift "garage"—pieces of tin nailed across some poles—holding my bow and arrow and looking out toward the fields, I feel an incredible blow in my right eye. I look down just in time to see my brother lower his gun.

Both brothers rush to my side. My eye stings, and I cover it with my hand. "If you tell," they say, "we will get a whipping. You don't want that to happen, do you?" I do not. "Here is a piece of wire," says the older brother, picking it up from the roof; "say you stepped on one end of it and the other flew up and hit you." The pain is beginning to start. "Yes," I say. "Yes, I will say that is what happened." If I do not say this is what happened, I know my brothers will find ways to make me wish I had. But now I will say anything that gets me to my mother.

Would I lie like this to protect my brothers?

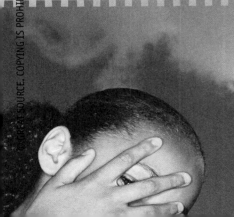

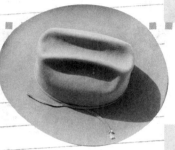

Confronted by our parents we stick to the lie agreed upon. They place me on a bench on the porch and I close my left eye while they examine the right. There is a tree growing from underneath the porch that climbs past the railing to the roof. It is the last thing my right eye sees. I watch as its trunk, its branches, and then its leaves are blotted out by the rising blood.

. . . Where the BB pellet struck there is a glob of whitish scar tissue, a hideous cataract, on my eye. Now when I stare at people—a favorite pastime, up to now—they will stare back. Not at the "cute" little girl, but at her scar. For six years I do not stare at anyone, because I do not raise my head.

Walker goes on to describe several memories that illustrate a lifelong struggle to accept the scar that resulted from the "accident." Continue reading and recording your connections.

But mostly, I remember this:

I am twenty-seven, and my baby daughter is almost three. Since her birth I have worried about her discovery that her mother's eyes are different from other people's. Will she be embarrassed? I think. What will she say? Every day she watches a television program called "Big Blue Marble." It begins with a picture of the earth as it appears from the moon. It is bluish, a little battered-looking, but full of light, with whitish clouds swirling around it. Every time I see it I weep with love, as if it is a picture of Grandma's house. One day when I am putting Rebecca down for her nap, she suddenly focuses on my eye. Something inside me cringes, gets ready to try to protect myself. All children are cruel about physical differences, I know from experience, and that they don't always mean to be is another matter. I assume Rebecca will be the same.

But no-o-o-o. She studies my face intently as we stand, her inside and me outside her crib. She even holds my face maternally between her dimpled little hands. Then, looking every bit as serious and lawyerlike as her father, she says, as if it may just possibly have slipped my attention: "Mommy, there's a world in your eye." (As in, "Don't be alarmed, or do anything crazy.") And then, gently, but with great interest: "Mommy, where did you get that world in your eye?"

For the most part, the pain left then. . . . Crying and laughing I ran to the bathroom, while Rebecca mumbled and sang herself off to sleep. Yes indeed, I realized, looking into the mirror. There was a world in my eye. And I saw that it was possible to love it: that in fact, for all it had taught me of shame and anger and inner vision, I did love it. ❖

✳ Memory as it is imagined, recounted, and written involves creating images and descriptions that **reconstruct** important moments in time. Working across the four memoirs, choose particularly vivid moments from each and explain how the images and descriptions help connect you to the events.

_____

_____

_____

_____

_____

_____

_____

_____

_____

_____

_____

_____

_____

_____

_____

_____

_____

_____

_____

_____

_____

_____

What does making connections between different memoirs contribute to your understanding of the meaning and importance of certain life experiences?

CONNECTING THROUGH WRITING

The authors of the memoirs you read in this unit recalled or reconstructed memories from when they were very young. Some recalled the details very accurately, such as Alice Walker remembering the accident that scarred her for life. Others told their stories in ways that maintained the *meaning* the stories have to them, even if the details are not historically accurate. Either way, it is in the selection of details and the choice of words that the stories truly represent their authors. Each writer carefully chose words that not only conveyed what *happened*, but also suggested, sometimes subtly and sometimes directly, the importance of the event on her life. This is the key to memoir.

Choose a memory that you would like to turn into a memoir. It may be a striking incident like Alice Walker's, a significant moment like a birthday, or a regular day that illustrates a significant time in your life, like Isabel Allende's. You may use a memory from your **Memory Catalog,** the memory you described on page 48, or any other meaningful memory you have recalled. Answer the following three prompts to help you get started.

1 Briefly describe the facts: When and where was the event. What was going on, or what happened?

_____

_____

_____

_____

_____

2 Describe some interesting, specific details: What you were wearing? What you were thinking about? What you could hear, see, and smell?

_____

_____

_____

_____

_____

_____

_____

3 Reflect on the meaning of this memory, just as Alice Walker does in the final paragraph of the selection from *In Search of Our Mother's Gardens* in Lesson 14. Why is this memory meaningful to you?

_____

_____

_____

_____

_____

_____

_____

_____

_____

✳ Tell the story to a partner. Invite your partner to ask questions that help you add more details to the event. Then, use the space here to either sketch or describe three key scenes from your memory.

✳ **Use your notes on pages 52–53 to draft your memoir.**

_____

_____

_____

_____

_____

_____

_____

_____

_____

_____

_____

_____

_____

_____

_____

_____

_____

_____

_____

_____

_____

_____

How has your understanding
of memoir changed as
a result of writing your
own memoir?

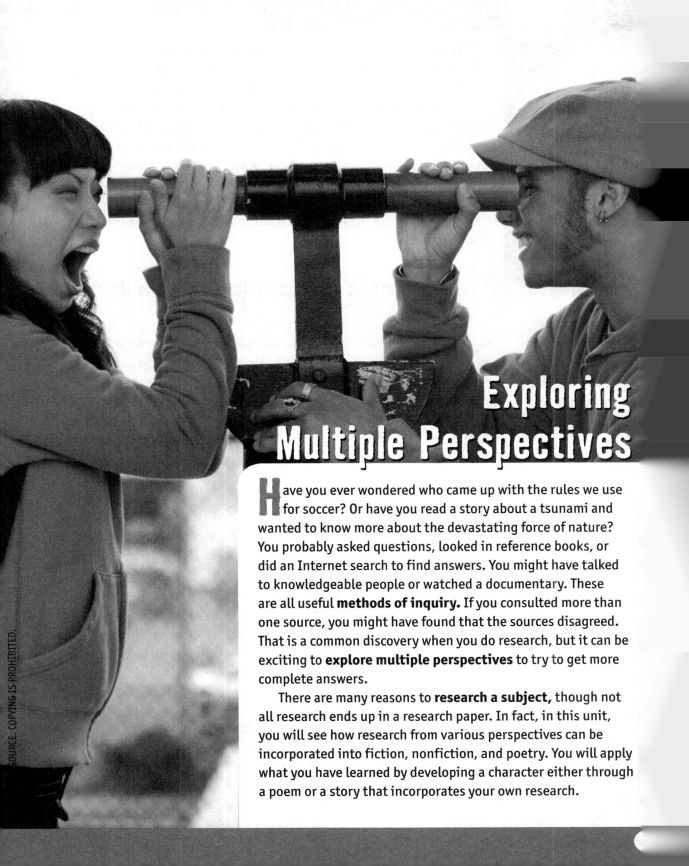

Exploring Multiple Perspectives

Have you ever wondered who came up with the rules we use for soccer? Or have you read a story about a tsunami and wanted to know more about the devastating force of nature? You probably asked questions, looked in reference books, or did an Internet search to find answers. You might have talked to knowledgeable people or watched a documentary. These are all useful **methods of inquiry.** If you consulted more than one source, you might have found that the sources disagreed. That is a common discovery when you do research, but it can be exciting to **explore multiple perspectives** to try to get more complete answers.

There are many reasons to **research a subject,** though not all research ends up in a research paper. In fact, in this unit, you will see how research from various perspectives can be incorporated into fiction, nonfiction, and poetry. You will apply what you have learned by developing a character either through a poem or a story that incorporates your own research.

What makes you curious? Do you want to know how things work or where something comes from? For many of us, the desire to find out why something happened leads to research to try to figure out answers.

That is the case for Christopher John Francis Boone, age 15. He is the main character of a contemporary **novel.** He lives with his father in Swindon, England, where he tries to solve a mystery. He also writes a book for his class. Read the opening chapter of his book to learn what the mystery is. It is helpful to know that in England, a garden fork is what people in the United States call a *pitchfork*.

As you read, use the **Response Notes** column to ask questions about the story.

Response Notes

Why was Christopher outside after midnight?

from The Curious Incident of the Dog in the Night-Time
by Mark Haddon

It was 7 minutes after midnight. The dog was lying on the grass in the middle of the lawn in front of Mrs. Shears's house. Its eyes were closed. It looked as if it was running on its side, the way dogs run when they think they are chasing a cat in a dream. But the dog was not running or asleep. The dog was dead. There was a garden fork sticking out of the dog. The points of the fork must have gone all the way through the dog and into the ground because the fork had not fallen over. I decided that the dog was probably killed with the fork because I could not see any other wounds in the dog and I do not think you would stick a garden fork into a dog after it had died for some other reason, like cancer, for example, or a road accident. But I could not be certain about this.

I went through Mrs. Shears's gate, closing it behind me. I walked onto her lawn and knelt beside the dog. I put my hand on the muzzle of the dog. It was still warm.

The dog was called Wellington. It belonged to Mrs. Shears, who was our friend. She lived on the opposite side of the road, two houses to the left.

Wellington was a poodle. Not one of the small poodles that have hairstyles but a big poodle. It had curly black fur, but when you got close you could see that the skin underneath the fur was a very pale yellow, like chicken.

I stroked Wellington and wondered who had killed him, and why.

✳ What is your first impression of Christopher? Write three words that describe him.

_____

✳ Discuss with a partner the steps you think Christopher should take to find out who killed Wellington. Record your notes here.

_____

_____

_____

How Christopher tries to solve the mystery depends in part on his personality. You can learn more about Christopher from what he says about what he likes and dislikes. As you read the following excerpt, underline or highlight the statements in which Christopher tells what he likes and dislikes and why. In this chapter, he mentions his teacher, Siobhan, and the school psychologist, Mr. Jeavons. He uses footnotes in his book to add information.

This is a murder mystery novel.

Siobhan said that I should write something I would want to read myself. Mostly I read books about science and maths. I do not like proper novels. In proper novels people say things like, "I am veined with iron, with silver and with streaks of common mud. I cannot contract into the firm fist which those clench who do not depend on stimulus."[1] What does this mean? I do not know. Nor does Father. Nor does Siobhan or Mr. Jeavons. I have asked them.

Siobhan has long blond hair and wears glasses which are made of green plastic. And Mr. Jeavons smells of soap and wears brown shoes that have approximately 60 tiny circular holes in each of them.

But I do like murder mystery novels. So I am writing a murder mystery novel.

In a murder mystery novel someone has to work out who the murderer is and then catch them. It is a puzzle. If it is a good puzzle you can sometimes work out the answer before the end of the book.

Siobhan said that the book should begin with something to grab people's attention. That is why I started with the dog. I also started with the dog because it happened to me and I find it hard to imagine things which did not happen to me.

_____

[1] I found this in a book when Mother took me into the library in town in 1996.

Siobhan read the first page and said that it was different. She put this word into inverted commas by making the wiggly quotation sign with her first and second fingers. She said that it was usually people who were killed in murder mystery novels. I said that two dogs were killed in *The Hound of the Baskervilles,* the hound itself and James Mortimer's spaniel, but Siobhan said they weren't the victims of the murder, Sir Charles Baskerville was. She said that this was because readers cared more about people than dogs, so if a person was killed in a book, readers would want to carry on reading.

I said that I wanted to write about something real and I knew people who had died but I did not know any people who had been killed, except Mr. Paulson, Edward's father from school, and that was a gliding accident, not murder, and I didn't really know him. I also said that I cared about dogs because they were faithful and honest, and some dogs were cleverer and more interesting than some people. Steve, for example, who comes to the school on Thursdays, needs help to eat his food and could not even fetch a stick. Siobhan asked me not to say this to Steve's mother. ❖

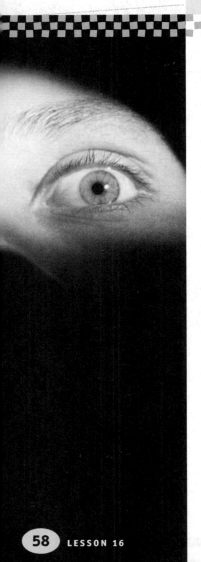

✳ Christopher himself is something of a mystery. What do you wonder about Christopher? Does he say anything that seems unusual? Make notes about what seems even a little surprising.

※ Use the Character Clues Puzzle to record what you know so far about Christopher. On each puzzle piece, write one thing that Christopher said about himself. On the lines, write **inferences,** or reasonable guesses, that you've made about Christopher's personality.

What are some ways that you can find answers when you are curious?

Christopher is a big fan of Sherlock Holmes mysteries. Both he and Holmes share an unconventional way of looking at the world. Sherlock Holmes often solves cases by making logical deductions from evidence that other people overlook, such as an old shoe or a silk rope. His perspective allows him to see the importance of what others do not see.

Christopher has an unconventional perspective on subjects because of who he is. If you saw him, you would say he looks like anyone else. However, if you were around him for very long, you might be curious about some of his behaviors and attitudes. In Lesson 16, did you wonder why Siobhan has to tell Christopher not to tell Steve's mother that Steve couldn't even fetch a stick? Christopher is incapable of understanding how hurtful that comment could be to Steve's mother.

What makes Christopher's **perspective** unconventional? He has a specific disability, although it is never named in the book. You might get some idea of how it affects him from his list of "Behavioral Problems" in this passage. Use the **Response Notes** to make notes about Christopher's behavior.

Response Notes

from **The Curious Incident of the Dog in the Night-Time**
by Mark Haddon

I used to think that Mother and Father might get divorced. That was because they had lots of arguments and sometimes they hated each other. This was because of the stress of looking after someone who has Behavioral Problems like I have. I used to have lots of Behavioral Problems, but I don't have so many now because I'm more grown up and I can take decisions for myself and do things on my own like going out of the house and buying things at the shop at the end of the road.

These are some of my Behavioral Problems
A. Not talking to people for a long time [4]
B. Not eating or drinking anything for a long time [5]
C. Not liking being touched
D. Screaming when I am angry or confused
E. Not liking being in really small places with other people
F. Smashing things when I am angry or confused
G. Groaning
H. Not liking yellow things or brown things and refusing to touch yellow things or brown things
I. Refusing to use my toothbrush if anyone else has touched it

Little kids do this

J. Not eating food if different sorts of food are touching each other

© GREAT SOURCE. COPYING IS PROHIBITED.

K. Not noticing that people are angry with me

L. Not smiling

M. Saying things that other people think are rude [6]

N. Doing stupid things [7]

O. Hitting other people

P. Hating France

Q. Driving Mother's car [8]

R. Getting cross when someone has moved the furniture [9] ❖

---

[4] Once I didn't talk to anyone for 5 weeks.

[5] When I was 6 Mother used to get me to drink strawberry-flavored slimming meals out of a measuring jug and we would have competitions to see how fast I could drink a quarter of a liter.

[6] People say that you always have to tell the truth. But they do not mean this because you are not allowed to tell old people that they are old and you are not allowed to tell people if they smell funny or if a grown-up has made a fart. And you are not allowed to say "I don't like you" unless that person has been horrible to you.

[7] Stupid things are things like emptying a jar of peanut butter onto the table in the kitchen and making it level with a knife so it covers all the table right to the edges, or burning things on the gas stove to see what happened to them, like my shoes or silver foil or sugar.

[8] I only did this once by borrowing the keys when she went into town on the bus, and I hadn't driven a car before and I was 8 years old and 5 months so I drove it into the wall, and the car isn't there anymore because Mother is dead.

[9] It is permitted to move the chairs and the table in the kitchen because that is different, but it makes me feel dizzy and sick if someone has moved the sofa and the chairs around in the living room or the dining room. Mother used to do this when she did the hoovering, so I made a special plan of where all the furniture was meant to be and did measurements and I put everything back in its proper place afterward and then I felt better. But since Mother died Father hasn't done any hoovering, so that is OK. And Mrs. Shears did the hoovering once but I did groaning and she shouted at Father and she never did it again.

✳ Discuss these behaviors with two other people. How does the list of behaviors help you develop a sense of the main character?

_____

_____

Christopher has Asperger's syndrome. Some consider it a mild form of autism. People who exhibit symptoms of Asperger's syndrome tend to have idiosyncratic interests, often focusing excessively on a single topic. The author, Mark Haddon, was an aide to autistic children at one time, and he has used what he learned about autism to create Christopher's character. He set out to create a believable, well-rounded character, not a character who represents people with Asperger's because, as he says, "people with Asperger's are as varied as Norwegians or trombone players."

✳ Try writing in Christopher's voice, using what you have read in Lessons 16 and 17. Write a short scene in which Christopher displays one or more of his "Behavioral Problems."

_____

_____

_____

_____

_____

_____

_____

_____

_____

_____

_____

_____

How can using an unconventional perspective help you understand a subject?

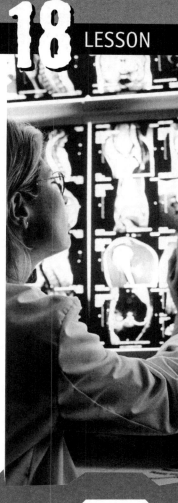

Scientists who study the brain add another **perspective** on the topic of autism. They are beginning to learn more, but much remains a mystery. What do you already know about autism? What are you curious about? Spend two minutes free-writing about these questions.

_____

_____

_____

_____

_____

_____

_____

_____

✳ Circle two topics in your free-writing that you are most curious about. As you read about autism, see if your questions are answered. In the **Response Notes,** make note of any information that is new to you. Also note connections to what you know about Christopher from Lesson 16 and 17.

from **Understanding Autism** by Geoffrey Cowley, Donna Foote, and Heather Won Tesoriero in *Newsweek,* 136.5 (July 31, 2000)

Autism stalks every sector of society, and its recognized incidence is exploding. In California, the number of kids receiving state services for autistic disorders has nearly quadrupled since 1987, rising 15 percent in the past three months alone. Nationally, the demand for such services rose by 556 percent during the '90s. Some experts see a growing epidemic in these numbers, while others believe they reflect new awareness of an existing problem. Either way, autism is now thought to affect one person in 500, making it more common than Down syndrome or childhood cancer. "This is not a rare disorder," says Dr. Marie Bristol Power of the National Institute of Child Health and Human Development (NICHD). "It's a pressing public-health problem."

And a profound mystery. Nearly six decades after autism was first formally recognized, the big questions—What causes it? Can it be prevented or cured?—are still wide open. But the pace of discovery is accelerating. Scientists are gaining tantalizing insights into the autistic mind, with its odd capacity for genius as well as detachment. And though the suspected causes

Response Notes

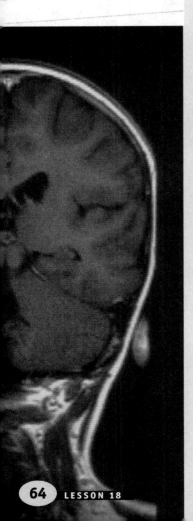

range from genetic mutations to viruses and toxic chemicals, we now know it's a brain-based developmental disorder and not a result of poor parenting (accepted wisdom as recently as the 1970s). The condition may never be eradicated, but science is making autistic life more livable, and enriching our whole understanding of the mind.

Until fairly recently, neuroscientists thought of autism as a single, utterly debilitating condition. . . . People with the classic form of the condition lack normal language ability, and they seem devoid of social impulses. A classically autistic child may tug on someone's arm to get a need met, but he (four out of five sufferers are male) won't spontaneously play peekaboo or share his delight in a toy. Nor will he engage in pretend play, using a banana, say, as a pistol or a telephone. What he will do is fixate on a pet interest—doorknobs, for instance, or license plates—and resist any change in routine. A new route to the grocery store can spark a major tantrum. Three out of four classically autistic people are thought to be mentally retarded. A third suffer from epilepsy, and most end up in institutions by the age of 13. . . .

As it turns out, though, autism has more than one face. During the 1940s, a Viennese pediatrician named Hans Asperger described a series of young patients who were somewhat autistic but still capable of functioning at a fairly high level. These "little professors" had quick tongues and sharp minds. They might stand too close and speak in loud monotones, but they could hold forth eloquently on their pet interests. Asperger's work went unread in the English-speaking world for several decades, but its rediscovery in the early 1980s started a revolution that is still unfolding. Experts now use terms like "Asperger disorder" and "pervasive development disorder" to describe mild variants of autism. And as the umbrella expands, more and more people are coming under it.

What, ultimately, makes autistic people different? How do they experience the world? Twenty years ago no one had much of a clue. But a burgeoning body of research now suggests that the core of all autism is a syndrome known as mindblindness. For most of us, mind reading comes as naturally as walking or chewing. We readily deduce what other people know and what they don't, and we understand implicitly that thoughts and feelings are revealed in gestures, facial expressions and tone of voice. An autistic person may sense none of this. . . .

It's not hard to see how mindblindness would derail a person's social development. If you can't perceive mental states, you can't show empathy, practice deceit or distinguish a joke from a threat—let alone make friends. Sharing becomes pointless when you can't see its effects on people, and conversation loses much of its meaning because you miss the unspoken intentions that hold it together. . . .

Romance is predictably difficult for autistic people, but many do brilliantly in certain lines of work. Only rarely does an autistic savant come along who can memorize a phone book in 10 minutes or measure the exact height of a building by glancing at it. But one autistic person in 10 shows exceptional skill in areas such as art, music, calculation or memory. . . .

People can build lives around these talents. Thirty-one-year-old Eric Spencer of Flemington, N.J., started reading when he was 18 months old. His autism has always confined him to well-controlled environments; he lives near his parents, aided by a "life-skills coordinator." But his love of letters—individual letters—has been a lifeline. A local library has exhibited his calligraphy, and he sometimes visits nursery schools to carve children's names from poster board for them. To earn money, he sorts documents at Ortho-MacNeil Pharmaceuticals. "My job," he says, "is getting along perfectly." ❖

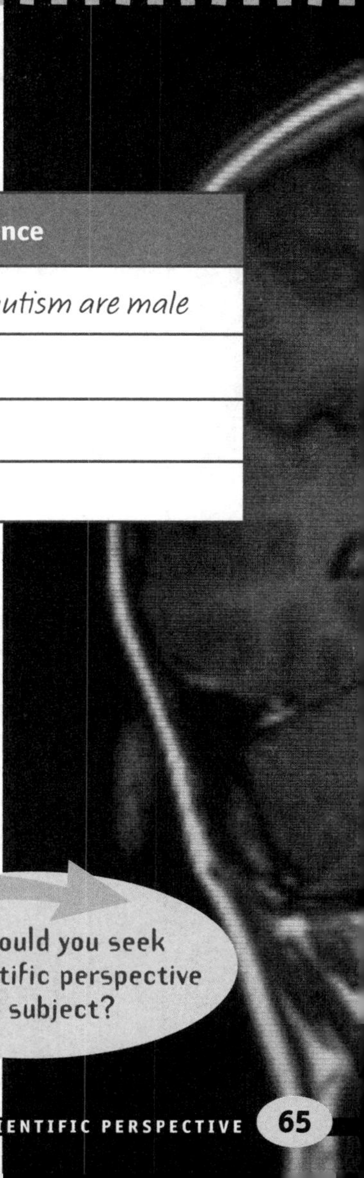

✳ The following chart will help you see how the scientific perspective is reflected in Mark Haddon's characterization of Christopher in Lessons 16 and 17. Use your Response Notes to fill in the chart.

Details about Christopher	Details from science
Male	Four out of five people with autism are male

✳ Discuss with a partner the differences between learning about a subject from a fictional perspective and from a scientific perspective. What are the advantages and disadvantages of each? What kind of information do you learn from each perspective? Which do you prefer and why? Record notes from your discussion here.

_____

_____

_____

_____

_____

When would you seek out a scientific perspective on a subject?

PERSONAL PERSPECTIVES

When you are looking for answers to your questions or acquiring new knowledge, you want to be sure that what you are learning is accurate and reliable. You need to consider the source. Remember that the perspective of the speaker or writer can determine what story gets told. It is usually best to get several different perspectives on a subject.

People who have experience with autism provide a perspective that scientists and fiction writers cannot. In this lesson, you will read two poems— one by the mother of an autistic boy and the other by an autistic boy.

As you read each poem, use the **Response Notes** to record your thinking, marking words and phrases that are surprising, striking, or somehow remarkable. Note lines in the poem from which you can make a personal connection to some element of your life or to something you have read.

Response Notes

Autism Poem: The Grid by Barbara Crooker

A black and yellow spider hangs motionless in its web,
and my son, who is eleven and doesn't talk, sits
on a patch of grass by the perennial border, watching.
What does he see in his world, where geometry
is more beautiful than a human face?
Given chalk, he draws shapes on the driveway:
pentagons, hexagons, rectangles, squares.
The spider's web is a grid,
transecting the garden in equal parts.

Sometimes he stares through the mesh on a screen.
He loves things that are perforated:
toilet paper, graham crackers, coupons
in magazines, loves the order of the tiny holes,
the way the boundaries are defined. And real life
is messy and vague. He shrinks back to a stare,
switches off his hearing. And my heart,
not cleanly cut like a valentine, but irregular
and many-chambered, expands and contracts,
contracts and expands. ❖

✳ What is your initial impression of this poem?

_____

_____

_____

_____

✳ Draw what some part of the world looks like to Barbara Crooker's son,
according to her speculations. Use specific language in the poem to
guide your illustration. Consider using color or another technique to
convey mood or feeling.

Autism by Brett Shaw, age 11, for his mother's birthday

I am autistic.
I can't speak.
I can't write with a pencil.
I can't ask for the things I need or want.
People look at me funny.
I don't know why they do that.
I am a boy who wants to be okay.
I am smart and funny.
Will I get to learn things like other boys?
I want to learn everything.
When will my teachers let me learn?
I can type to answer questions.
I can write by typing.
I can do anything I want to do.
I can learn anything I want to learn.
I am Brett Shaw. ❖

Because he has a difficult time focusing, it took Brett two days to type this poem with the help of a facilitator who was working with him. Since he has learned to type, he can communicate and can show that he understands spoken language, which wasn't apparent before.

What does a personal perspective add that no other perspective can?

You have read about people who see the world differently from how most people see it. From what you have read, you know that there are many different kinds of people who are labeled *autistic* and that some of these people excel at certain tasks while they are not as good at others. You have also seen how different perspectives provide different information about a person. The view of an author constructing a fictional character such as Christopher may vary from that of the mother of an autistic child imagining what her child sees. Scientists, through a variety of studies, have revealed commonalities and differences among people with autism.

In this lesson, you will research a disorder or disability to find information from different perspectives. Then you will create a character based on your research. Begin with your curiosity. What do you want to know more about—Down syndrome, childhood cancer, dyslexia, bipolar disorder, or something else? What perspectives are available—scientific research, personal accounts, fictional portrayals? The idea chart on this page will help you gather and organize the ideas from your research.

Name, gender, age	
Disorder, disability, or disease	
Likes	
Dislikes	
What he/she does when ■ **frustrated** ■ **happy** ■ **sad** ■ **afraid**	
Special talents	

✳ Use this page to draft a character profile. You have three choices for a way to present your character. You can describe the person, incorporating relevant information from your planning chart. You can show the person in action, creating a realistic setting, adding dialogue and other characters. You can write a poem or narrative from the point of view of a relative or of the character.

_____

_____

_____

_____

_____

_____

_____

_____

_____

_____

_____

_____

_____

_____

_____

_____

_____

_____

_____

_____

_____

_____

_____

What does an author need to consider when using research to create an imaginary character?

_____

_____

_____

Focusing on Language and Craft

Why is the sky blue? Where does the sun go at night? How do birds fly? **Questions** come naturally to us when we're children and the world seems new. As we grow older, however, we often replace questions with assumptions. We think we know the answers to our questions; we sometimes assume we know things when we really need to ask in order to learn.

Questions are at the heart of learning. We need to learn how to ask them and to follow up with deeper questions related to the ideas they provoke. Sometimes writers pose questions when they want readers to participate in their own explorations. Statements may provoke our own thoughts, but they tell us what the speaker or writer already thinks. Questions, on the other hand, invite us to see possibilities that we hadn't thought of before.

It is through questioning that we can keep our minds alive to new ideas.

LESSON 21 — QUESTIONS WITHOUT ANSWERS

The game Twenty Questions, which you may have played, is based on asking yes or no questions to identify a person, a place, or a thing. What kinds of attributes might you guess to identify the nature of an object?

✳ Write a few suggestions here:

_____

_____

In the poem "Twenty Questions," Donald Justice plays a different kind of game. Read the poem once just to get a first impression. Then read it again and use the **Response Notes** column to respond to the poet's questions with answers and your own questions.

Response Notes

How did someone think of all these questions?

Twenty Questions by Donald Justice

Is it raining out?
Is it raining in?
Are you a public fountain?
Are you an antique musical instrument?
Are you a famous resort, perhaps?
What is your occupation?
Are you by chance a body of water?
Do you often travel alone?
What is your native language, then?
Do you recall the word for carnation?

Are you sorry?
Will you be sorry?
Is this your handkerchief?
What is your destination?
Are you Aquarius?
Are you the watermelon flower?
Will you please take off your glasses?
Is this a holiday for you?
Is that a scar, or a birthmark?
Is there no word for calyx in your tongue? ✤

QUESTIONING THE QUESTIONS

✳ Into what categories do the poet's questions fit? With a partner, try to categorize as many of the questions as you can. Don't get too serious about this; use your creativity to make up categories. Write the names of your categories in the table and list the questions that fit under each. For example, under the category Personal, you might list "Is that a scar or a birthmark?" Other categories might be Impersonal, Logical, or Nonsensical.

CATEGORY CHART

_____	_____	_____	_____

✳ With a partner, create an occasion for a conversation in which the speaker of the poem might ask the "you" of the poem some of these questions. Describe the occasion for the conversation. Tell who the two people might be.

Occasion: _____

Two people who might have the conversation: _____

    Who is the speaker? _____

    Who is the "you" of the poem? _____

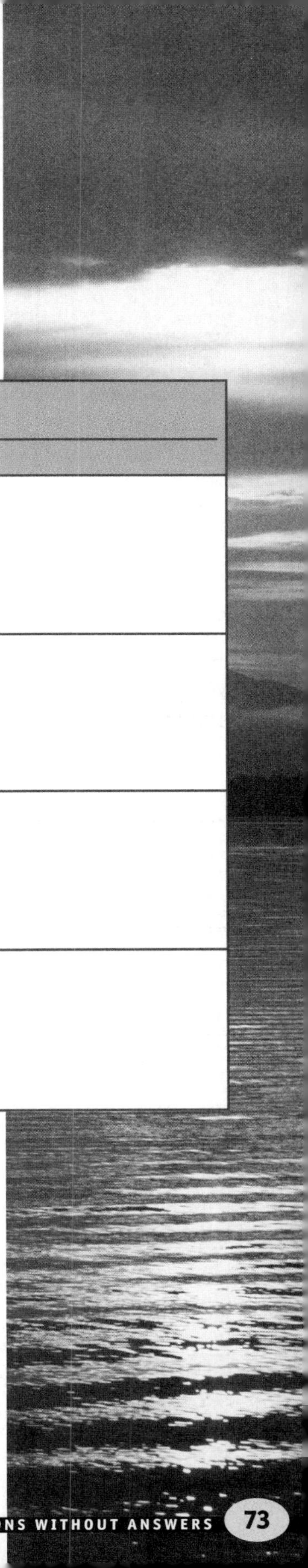

＊ Write a dialogue between the speaker and the "you," aligning the response lines to the right of the speaker lines. Use your **Response Notes** for ideas. (Remember that the "you" of the poem may respond with another question as well as a statement.) Use at least eight of the questions in your dialogue.

First Speaker _____   Second Speaker _____

Copy lines of the poem here	Write the responses here
Example: Is it raining out?	It sounds like it, but there are no windows, so I can't see.

How can asking nonsense questions lead to real meaning?

MAKING CONNECTIONS

Making connections with what we read is an important strategy. In this lesson, you will practice **making connections** with ideas that are both childlike and serious. Sometimes poets play with language as a way of making you think in creative ways. That's what Pablo Neruda does in the poems you will read in the next two lessons.

Pablo Neruda (right), a Chilean poet, was also a politician. He won a Nobel Prize for his poetry but was exiled from his country for his politics. The movie *Il Postino,* or *The Postman,* shows part of his life in exile. Neruda's poems reflect his ideas about life and politics. The poems in this unit are from his book called *The Book of Questions.* All the poems in this book are composed in question form.

As you read these three poems by Neruda, write your own questions, connections, and annotations in the **Response Notes** column.

Poems VII, XVI, and XXIV by Pablo Neruda

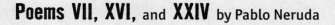

VII

Is peace the peace of the dove?
Does the leopard wage war?

Why does the professor teach
the geography of death?

What happens to swallows
who are late for school?

Is it true they scatter
transparent letters across the sky?

XVI

Do salt and sugar work
to build a white tower?

Is it true that in an anthill
dreams are a duty?

Do you know what the earth
meditates upon in autumn?

(Why not give a medal
to the first golden leaf?)

Response Notes

What makes the dove a symbol of peace?

XXIV

Is 4 the same 4 for everybody?
Are all sevens equal?

When the convict ponders the light
is it the same light that shines on you?

For the diseased, what color
do you think April is?

Which occidental monarchy
will fly flags of poppies?

1 Reread Neruda's poems. To which poem did you make the strongest connection? What were the connections?

_____

_____

_____

_____

2 Use the connections to spin off your own questions about a serious topic. Pose playful and hypothetical questions.

Questions
What if everyone in the world got along?

3 Use your questions to draft a poem. You might start your poem with *Imagine* or *What if*.

_____

_____

_____

_____

_____

_____

4 Read your draft. Mix up the questions to see if you like the flow better. Share your revised draft with a partner.

5 Revise your poem again by listening to the comments of several class-mates. Write a final draft and include a title.

_____

_____

_____

_____

_____

_____

_____

_____

_____

_____

_____

_____

_____

_____

_____

What is the value of making connections with what you read?

SEARCHING FOR MEANING IN POEMS

When we hear a question, our natural inclination is to respond. We do this even when the questions seem to have no answers, like the questions many young children, and some poets, ask. When the questions seem to have no direct answers, we may still attempt to respond. In the process of trying to answer what seem to be silly questions, we may come to an understanding we weren't expecting.

In this lesson you will read two additional Neruda question poems. Stop and respond after each one.

Poems **XXXI** and **XLIV** by Pablo Neruda

Response Notes

XXXI

Whom can I ask what I came
to make happen in this world?

Why do I move without wanting to,
why am I not able to sit still?

Why do I go rolling without wheels,
flying without wings or feathers,

and why did I decide to migrate
if my bones live in Chile?

✳ If you were the poet, how might you answer the first question in this poem?

_____

_____

_____

_____

✳ Have you ever asked questions to which there are no answers? Why do people sometimes pose such questions?

_____

_____

_____

_____

XLIV

Stanza 1

Where is the child I was,
still inside me or gone?

Stanza 2

Does he know that I never loved him
and that he never loved me?

Stanza 3

Why did we spend so much time
growing up only to separate?

Stanza 4

Why did we both not die
when my childhood died?

Stanza 5

And why does my skeleton pursue me
if my soul has fallen away? ❖

✳ Select one of the first four stanzas and write about what it could mean.

Number of the stanza you are writing about: _____

_____

_____

_____

_____

_____

_____

_____

_____

✳ What do you think the last stanza means? On what did you base
   your answer?

_____

_____

_____

_____

_____

_____

✳ Try writing a response to one or more stanzas of this poem, either as
   another poem or as prose. If you choose prose, you might write it as a
   letter to a specific person.

_____

_____

_____

_____

_____

_____

_____

_____

_____

_____

_____

_____

_____

How has your understanding
of seemingly nonsensical poems
changed as a result of reading
these Neruda poems?

_____

_____

_____

_____

How do we learn new things? One way is through the use of **similes.** Similes are comparisons that help us to deal with the unknown in terms of the known. In "Some Questions You Might Ask," the poet Mary Oliver uses a simile in the form of a question to frame her poem about one of life's most intriguing abstractions: the soul.

Read the poem, asking your own questions as you read. Write your questions and reflections in the **Response Notes** column.

Some Questions You Might Ask by Mary Oliver

Is the soul solid, like iron?
Or is it tender and breakable, like
the wings of a moth in the beak of the owl?
Who has it, and who doesn't?
I keep looking around me,
The face of the moose is as sad
as the face of Jesus.
The swan opens her white wings slowly.
In the fall, the black bear carries leaves into the darkness.
One question leads to another.
Does it have a shape? Like an iceberg?
Like the eye of a hummingbird?
Does it have one lung, like the snake and the scallop?
Why should I have it, and not the anteater
who loves her children?
Why should I have it, and not the camel?
Come to think of it, what about the maple trees?
What about the blue iris?
What about all the little stones, sitting alone in the moonlight?
What about roses, and lemons, and their shining leaves?
What about the grass? ❖

Response Notes

Do I know for sure that I have a soul?

✳ Reread the poem, this time looking carefully at all the comparisons Oliver makes between the soul, or some aspect of the soul, and familiar objects. Notice that Oliver makes a number of direct connections using the words *like* or *as,* which often indicate a simile.

✳ In the following chart, list at least three similes you can find in the poem. In the right column, explain the quality of the soul referred to in the simile.

Is the soul like . . .	What quality forms the basis for the comparison?
Example: iron	solid

✳ When Oliver writes that "One question leads to another," she first deals with whether the soul has a shape. Then she asks a series of questions about the animals or things that she thinks have or should have souls. What do you think Oliver means by the word *soul* as she uses it in this poem?

_____

_____

_____

_____

_____

_____

_____

_____

_____

_____

_____

_____

How do similes
help you derive meaning
from a poem?

Mary Oliver, whose poetry you read in Lesson 24, also used questions to clarify as the basis for her poem called "What Is It?" Read the poem and think about your response to it. Write your questions and comments in the **Response Notes** column.

What Is It? by Mary Oliver

Who can say,
is it a snowy egret
or a white flower
standing

at the glossy edge
of the lily-
and frog-filled pond?
Hours ago the orange sun

opened the cups of the lilies
and the leopard frogs
began kicking
their long muscles,

breast-stroking
like little green dwarves
under the roof of the rich,
iron-colored water.

Now the soft
eggs of the salamander
in their wrappings of jelly
begin to shiver.

They're tired of sleep.
They have a new idea.
They want to swim away
into the world.

Who could stop them?
Who could tell them
to go cautiously, to flow slowly
under the lily pads?

Response Notes

Why does the author choose two white objects for the first stanza?

Off they go,
hundreds of them,
like the black
fingerprints of the rain.

The frogs freeze
into perfect five-fingered
shadows, but suddenly the flower
has fire-colored eyes

and one of the shadows vanishes.
Clearly, now, the flower is a bird.
It lifts its head,
it lifts the hinges

of its snowy wings,
tossing a moment of light
in every direction
like a chandelier,

and then once more is still.
The salamanders,
like tiny birds, locked into formation,
fly down into the endless mysteries

of the transforming water,
and how could anyone believe
that anything in this world
is only what it appears to be—

that anything is ever final—
that anything, in spite of its absence,
ever dies
a perfect death? ❖

✳ What do you think this poem is about? At this point, you may have more questions than answers. Writing what you think it is about will help you work through the other questions about the poem.

_____

_____

_____

_____

_____

_____

_____

_____

_____

_____

_____

_____

✳ This poem can be visualized in three scenes: the beginning, the action, and afterwards. Draw sketches of these scenes that show how you visualize what the words depict.

The beginning	The event	Afterwards

✳ Compare your drawings with a classmate's drawings. Talk about the questions either of you has about the poem. Review your original questions and comments. Be sure that you deal with remaining concerns about the meaning of the poem. Make notes about your conversation here.

_____

_____

_____

_____

_____

_____

_____

_____

_____

_____

✳ Review your Response Notes and think about any personal connections in order to write a response to Oliver's final question ("How could anyone believe . . . ?").

_____

_____

_____

_____

_____

_____

_____

_____

_____

_____

How does a poet's use of language and craft affect your experience of a poem?

_____

_____

_____

_____

Studying an Author

When you read a novel or short story by **Ursula K. Le Guin,** you are likely to read about life in imaginary worlds such as Gethen or the twin planets of Werel and Yeowe at the far end of our universe. You find interstellar travelers, starships, and faster-than-light communication in her science fiction. And you encounter dragons and wizards in the kingdom of Earthsea in her fantasy.

Le Guin has written novels, short stories, books for children, poetry, and essays. She has won numerous literary awards for her out-of-this-world imaginings. Le Guin believes fiction should offer readers the chance to experience new worlds— worlds in the past, worlds in imaginary places, worlds in minds different from their own.

In this unit, you will inquire into the work of this celebrated writer, exploring techniques that she and other writers of **fantasy** use. They hope to convince their readers that their imaginary worlds are believable.

Why are we interested in novels or films that take us into **fantasy** worlds, the future, or outer space? Why is it that we will believe, temporarily at least, in such worlds? Long before J. K. Rowling or Christopher Paolini, writers invited their readers to journey through galaxies, come face-to-face with aliens, and believe in magical swords, talking animals, and imaginary lands.

Le Guin specializes in these kinds of stories—what she calls "thought experiments." For both writer and reader, thought–experiment stories require participation in the "believing game"—a willingness to suspend, temporarily, the rules of the known world. Examine how Le Guin introduces a new world in her novel. Circle some of the details that separate this place—the people, animals, or landscape—from ones that you would expect to find in the world you know. In your **Response Notes,** explain whether these details help you believe in this imaginary place.

Response Notes

from **The Eye of the Heron** by Ursula K. Le Guin

In the sunlight in the center of a ring of trees Lev sat cross-legged, his head bent above his hands.

A small creature crouched in the warm, shallow cup of his palms. He was not holding it; it had decided or consented to be there. It looked like a little toad with wings. The wings, folded into a peak above its back, were dun-colored with shadowy streaks, and its body was shadow-colored. Three gold eyes like large pinheads adorned its head, one on each side and one in the center of the skull. This upward-looking central eye kept watch on Lev. Lev blinked. The creature changed. Dusty pinkish fronds sprouted out from under its folded wings. For a moment it appeared to be a feathery ball, hard to see clearly, for the fronds or feathers trembled continually, blurring its outlines. Gradually the blur died away. The toad with wings sat there as before, but now it was light blue. It scratched its left eye with the hindmost of its three left feet. Lev smiled. Toad, wings, eyes, legs vanished. A flat moth-like shape crouched on Lev's palm, almost invisible because it was, except for some shadowy patches, exactly the same color and texture as his skin. He sat motionless. Slowly the blue toad with wings reappeared, one golden eye keeping watch on him. It walked across his palm and up the curve of his fingers. The six tiny, warm feet gripped and released, delicate and precise. It paused on the tip of his fingers and cocked its head to look at him with its right eye while its left and central eyes scanned the sky. It gathered itself into an arrow shape, shot out two translucent underwings twice the length of its body, and flew off in a long effortless glide toward a sunlit slope beyond the ring of trees.

"Lev?"

"Entertaining a wotsit." He got up, and joined Andre outside the tree-ring.

"Martin thinks we might get home tonight."

"Hope he's right," Lev said. He picked up his backpack and joined the end of the line of seven men. They set off in single file, not talking except when one down the line called to indicate to the leader a possible easier way to take, or when the second in line, carrying the compass, told the leader to bear right or left. Their direction was southwestward. The going was not hard, but there was no path and there were no landmarks. The trees of the forest grew in circles, twenty to sixty trees forming a ring around a clear central space. In the valleys of the rolling land the tree-rings grew so close, often interlocking, that the travelers' way was a constant alternation of forcing through undergrowth between dark shaggy trunks, clear going across spongy grass in the sunlit circle, then again shade, foliage, crowded stems and trunks. On the hillsides the rings grew farther apart, and sometimes there was a long view over winding valleys endlessly dappled with the soft rough red circles of the trees.

As the afternoon wore on a haze paled the sun. Clouds thickened from the west. A fine, small rain began to fall. It was mild, windless. The travelers' bare chests and shoulders shone as if oiled. Water drops clung in their hair. They went on, bearing steadily south by west. The light grew grayer. In the valleys, in the circles of the trees, the air was misty and dark.

The lead man, Martin, topping a long stony rise of land, turned and called out. One by one they climbed up and stood beside him on the crest of the ridge. Below a broad river lay shining and colorless between dark beaches.

The eldest of them, Holdfast, got to the top last and stood looking down at the river with an expression of deep satisfaction. "Hullo there," he murmured, as to a friend.

"Which way to the boats?" asked the lad with the compass.

"Upstream," Martin said, tentative.

"Down," Lev proposed. "Isn't that the high point of the ridge, west there?"

They discussed it for a minute and decided to try downstream. For a little longer before they went on they stood in silence on the ridge top, from which they had a greater view of the world than they had had for many days. Across the river the forest rolled on southward in endless interlocking ring patterns under hanging clouds. Eastward, upriver, the land rose steeply; to the west the river wound in gray levels between lower hills. Where it disappeared from sight a faint brightness lay upon it, a hint of sunlight on the open sea. Northward, behind the travelers' backs, the forested hills, the days and miles of their journey, lay darkening into the rain and night.

In all that immense, quiet landscape of hills, forest, river, no thread of smoke; no house; no road. ❖

Imagine that you have been asked to design the cover for this novel. What do you know about Le Guin's world that you would want to include? Draw a cover that emphasizes her world as you imagine it.

How does the author convince you that the fantasy elements of the story are somehow believable?

L e Guin gives an assignment to her writing workshop students that requires them to invent an artifact, or object, and think about how it might be used in a story. In the following story, Le Guin chose to use the artifact that her friend, Roussel Sargent, had created. Sargent named her artifact a *kerastion* and described it as "a musical instrument that cannot be heard." From this, Le Guin imagined a story.

from **The Kerastion** by Ursula K. Le Guin

Response Notes

The small caste of the Tanners was a sacred one. To eat food prepared by a Tanner would entail a year's purification to a Tinker or a Sculptor, and even low-power castes such as the Traders had to be cleansed by a night's ablutions after dealing for leather goods. Chumo had been a Tanner since she was five years old and had heard the willows whisper all night long at the Singing Sands. She had had her proving day, and since then had worn a Tanner's madder-red and blue shirt and doublet, woven of linen on a willow-wood loom. She had made her masterpiece, and since then had worn the Master Tanner's neckband of dried vauti-tuber incised with the double line and double circles. So clothed and so ornamented she stood among the willows by the burying ground, waiting for the funeral procession of her brother, who had broken the law and betrayed his caste. She stood erect and silent, gazing towards the village by the river and listening for the drum.

She did not think; she did not want to think. But she saw her brother Kwatewa in the reeds down by the river, running ahead of her, a little boy too young to have a caste, too young to be polluted by the sacred, a crazy little boy pouncing on her out of the tall reeds shouting, "I'm a mountain lion!"

A serious little boy watching the river run, asking, "Does it ever stop? Why can't it stop running, Chumo?"

A five-year-old coming back from the Singing Sands, coming straight to her, bringing her the joy, the crazy, serious joy that shone in his round face—"Chumo! I heard the sand singing! I heard it! I have to be a Sculptor, Chumo!"

She had stood still. She had not held out her arms. And he had checked his run towards her and stood still, the light going out of his face. She was only his wombsister. He would have truesibs, now. He and she were of different castes. They would not touch again.

Ten years after that day she had come with most of the townsfolk to Kwatewa's proving day, to see the sand-sculpture he had made in the Great Plain Place where the Sculptors performed their art. Not a breath of wind had yet rounded off the keen edges or leveled the lovely curves of the classic form he had executed with such verve and sureness, the Body of Amakumo. She saw admiration and envy in the faces of his truebrothers and truesisters. Standing aside among the sacred castes, she heard the speaker of the Sculptors dedicate Kwatewa's proving piece to Amakumo. As his voice ceased a wind came out of the desert north, Amakumo's wind, the maker hungry for the made—Amakumo the Mother eating her body, eating herself. Even while they watched, the wind destroyed Kwatewa's sculpture. Soon there was only a shapeless lump and a feathering of white sand blown across the proving ground. Beauty had gone back to the Mother. That the sculpture had been destroyed so soon and so utterly was a great honor to the maker.

The funeral procession was approaching. She heard or imagined she heard the drumbeat, soft, no more than a heartbeat. . . . ❖

❋ Le Guin must create a supporting world in which the kerastion develops some significance. List everything that you know about the society and its people. Explain what you think the information reveals about the world that Le Guin has imagined.

	What I know about	**What is revealed**
Society	*caste system by occupation*	*rules of behavior linked to caste*
People		

❋ Write two or three sentences speculating on how Le Guin will use the kerastion in the story.

_____

_____

_____

_____

_____

❋ Create an artifact of your own. Decide on its characteristics. Give the artifact a name. Write a ten-word sentence about your artifact in much the same way that Roussel Sargent did: "The kerastion is a musical instrument that cannot be heard." Then write the beginning of your story.

Ten-word sentence:

_____

_____

Beginning:

_____

_____

_____

_____

_____

_____

_____

_____

_____

_____

_____

_____

_____

_____

_____

_____

_____

_____

_____

_____

How can an author use an imaginary object to add layers of meaning to the story?

Fantasy invites readers to fasten their seatbelts for a fast-paced journey into a seemingly impossible world. Where do ideas for **fantasy** come from? Early in her writing career, Le Guin found the subject for one of her fantasy stories in something her daughter said. In her introduction to the following story, Le Guin writes about what sparked the idea:

> When my daughter Caroline was three she came to me with a small wooden box in her small hands and said, "Guess fwat is in this bockus!" I guessed caterpillars, mice, elephants, etc. She shook her head, smiled an unspeakably eldritch smile, opened the box slightly so that I could just see in, and said: "Darkness." Hence, this story.

A successful writer of fantasy blends reality with fantasy. As you read, note parts of the story that seem believable and parts that don't. Highlight them in the text or make notes in the **Response Notes.**

Response Notes

from **Darkness Box** by Ursula K. Le Guin

On soft sand by the sea's edge a little boy walked leaving no footprints. Gulls cried in the bright sunless sky, trout leaped from the saltless ocean. Far off on the horizon the sea serpent raised himself a moment in seven enormous arches and then, bellowing, sank. The child whistled but the sea serpent, busy hunting whales, did not surface again. The child walked on casting no shadow, leaving no tracks on the sand between the cliffs and the sea. Ahead of him rose a grassy headland on which stood a four-legged hut. As he climbed a path up the cliff the hut skipped about and rubbed its front legs together like a lawyer or a fly; but the hands of the clock inside, which said ten minutes of ten, never moved.

"What's that you've got there, Dicky?" asked his mother as she added parsley and a pinch of pepper to the rabbit stew simmering in an alembic.

"A box, Mummy."

"Where did you find it?"

Mummy's familiar leaped down from the onion-festooned rafters and, draping itself like a foxfur round her neck, said, "By the sea."

Dicky nodded. "That's right. The sea washed it up."

"And what's inside it?"

The familiar said nothing, but purred. The witch turned round to look into her son's round face. "What's in it?" she repeated.

"Darkness."

"Oh, Let's see."

As she bent down to look the familiar, still purring, shut its eyes. Holding the box against his chest, the little boy very carefully lifted the lid a scant inch.

"So it is," said his mother. "Now put it away, don't let it get knocked about. I wonder where the key got to. Run wash your hands now. Table, lay!" And while the child worked the heavy pump-handle in the yard and splashed his face and hands, the hut resounded with the clatter of plates and forks materializing.

After the meal, while his mother was having her morning nap, Dicky took down the water-bleached, sand-encrusted box from his treasure shelf and set out with it across the dunes, away from the sea. Close at his heels the black familiar followed him, trotting patiently over the sand through the coarse grass, the only shadow he had.

At the summit of the pass Prince Rikard turned in the saddle to look back over the plumes and pennants of his army, over the long falling road, to the towered walls of his father's city. Under the sunless sky it shimmered there on the plain, fragile and shadowless as a pearl. Seeing it so he knew it could never be taken, and his heart sang with pride. He gave his captains the signal for quick march and set spurs to his horse. It reared and broke into a gallop, while his gryphon swooped and screamed overhead. She teased the white horse, diving straight down at it clashing her beak, swerving aside just in time; the horse, bridleless, would snap furiously at her snaky tail or rear to strike out with silver hoofs. The gryphon would cackle and roar, circle back over the dunes and with a screech and swoop play the trick all over. Afraid she might wear herself out before the battle, Rikard finally leashed her, after which she flew along steadily, purring and chirping, by his side.

The sea lay before him; somewhere beneath the cliffs the enemy force his brother led was hidden. The road wound down growing sandier, the sea appearing to right or left always nearer. Abruptly the road fell away; the white horse leaped the ten-foot drop and galloped out over the beach. As he came out from between the dunes Rikard saw a long line of men strung out on the sand, and behind them three black-prowed ships. His own men were scrambling down the drop, swarming over the dunes, blue flags snapping in the sea wind, voices faint against the sound of the sea.

[A battle ensues. After a difficult fight Rikard and his men push the attackers into the sea. Then, Rikard and his army head back toward the city.]

Taking an easier road homeward, Rikard passed not far from the four-legged hut on the headland. The witch stood in the doorway, hailing him. He galloped over, and, drawing rein right at the gate of the little yard, he looked at the young witch. She was bright and dark as coals, her black hair whipped in the sea wind. She looked at him, white-armored on a white horse.

"Prince," she said, "you'll go to battle once too often."

He laughed. "What should I do—let my brother lay siege to the city?"

"Yes, let him. No man can take the city."

I know. But my father the king exiled him, he must not set foot even on our shore. I'm my father's soldier, I fight as he commands."

The witch looked out to sea, then back at the young man. Her dark face sharpened, nose and chin peaking crone-like, eyes flashing. "Serve and be served," she said, "rule and be ruled. Your brother chose neither to serve nor rule. Listen, prince, take care." Her face warmed again to beauty. "The sea brings presents this morning, the wind blows, the crystals break. Take care."

Gravely he bowed his thanks, then wheeled his horse and was gone, white as a gull over the long curve on the dunes. ❖

✳ **Complete the following sentences.**

1 The character I identify most with is _____

because _____

2 The thing that is hardest to believe is _____

3 I think this story is about _____

4 This story reminds me of _____

5 The phrase that gives me the most information about what will happen in the story is _____

6 The story of the battle would be different without the witch because _____

7 The darkness in the box might represent _____

_____

8 The characteristics of fantasy that I noticed in the story are _____

_____

> What is the effect of the author's use of realistic elements to develop her imaginary world?

✳ Note how Le Guin uses a familiar, believable scene—a young boy at the beach—and accompanies it with elements of fantasy. For example, the boy leaves no footprints, and the hut skips. Use the **Response Notes** and your highlighting to discuss with a partner how the realistic elements help you believe in Le Guin's imaginary world.

L e Guin wrote in her introduction to *The Left Hand of Darkness*, "[Writers] may use all kinds of facts to support their tissue of lies." To compose a tissue of lies, the writer needs to include enough information to help the reader understand and believe in the society or world that has been created. Writers **extrapolate**—borrow facts, objects, ideas—from the real world to give a sense of reality to their fantastical worlds. Even the weakest of ties to the known world gives a story some believability.

✳ To help you think about Le Guin's use of extrapolation, write a few sentences in response to each of these questions, using examples from your reading in Lessons 26–28. Then discuss your responses with a partner.

■ In what ways does Le Guin extrapolate in order to ground her readers in the worlds of her imaginings?

_____

_____

_____

■ For example, what characteristics of the "creature" in *The Eye of the Heron* are exaggerations of natural, biological functions of an insect?

_____

_____

■ How effectively does Le Guin exaggerate these natural qualities?

_____

_____

_____

_____

_____

_____

_____

✳ Share your answers with a partner.

✳ Try your hand at extrapolating from the real world to create a "tissue of lies" about a fantastical world or society. The following questions will help you develop your ideas before you write a scene yourself.

1 Choose an object or place from which to extrapolate and describe it.

_____

_____

_____

2 On what characteristics will you exaggerate or build to create your story?

_____

_____

_____

3 What will be fantastical about your object or place?

_____

_____

_____

✳ Use your answers to write a draft of a scene that features your "tissue of lies."

_____

_____

_____

_____

_____

_____

_____

_____

How much reality should an author use to help readers make connections between the real world and story world?

_____

_____

_____

What makes one writer choose to write nonfiction and another fantasy? Read excerpts from the **speech** Le Guin made to the "Lost Worlds and Future Worlds" convention to get a better understanding of her reasons for writing about fantasy worlds.

from **World—Making** by Ursula K. Le Guin

Response Notes

To make something is to invent it, to discover it, to uncover it, like Michelangelo cutting away the marble that hid the statue. Perhaps we think less often of the proposition reversed, thus: To discover something is to make it. As Julius Caesar said, "the existence of Britain was uncertain, until I went there." We can safely assume that the ancient Britons were perfectly certain of the existence of Britain, down to such details as where to go for the best wood. But, as Einstein said, it all depends on how you look at it, and as far as Rome, not Britain, is concerned, Caesar invented (invenire, "to come into, to come upon") Britain. He made it be, for the rest of the world.

Alexander the Great sat down and cried, somewhere in the middle of India, I think, because there were no more new worlds to conquer. What a silly man he was. There he sits sniveling, halfway to China! A conqueror. Conquistadores, always running into new worlds, and quickly running out of them. Conquest is not finding, and it is not making our culture, which conquered what is called the New World, and which sees the world of nature as an adversary to be conquered: look at us now. Running out of everything.

The name of our meeting is Lost Worlds and Future Worlds. Whether our ancestors came seeking gold, or freedom, or as slaves, we are the conquerors, we who live here now, in possession, in the New World. We are the inhabitants of a Lost World. It is utterly lost. Even the names are lost. . . .

And one line is left of a dancing song:

Dancing on the brink of the world.

With such fragments I might have shored my ruin, but I didn't know how. Only knowing that we must have a past to make a future with, I took what I could from the European-based cultures of my own forefathers and mothers. I learned, like most of us, to use whatever I could, to filch an idea from China and steal a god from India, and so patch together a world as best I could. But still there is a mystery. This place where I was born and grew up and love beyond all other, my world, my California, still needs to be made. To make a new world you start with an old one certainly. To find a world maybe you have to have lost one. Maybe you have to be lost. The dance of renewal, the dance that made the world, was always danced here at the edge of things, on the brink, on the foggy coast. ✜

✳ Write a short response to each of the following questions:

■ What do you think the connection is between world-making and "dancing on the brink of the world"?

_____

■ What does Le Guin say about why she chooses to write fantasy?

■ What does she say about why she creates worlds from her imagination rather than trying to describe the world in which she lives?

_____

■ What other points does she make that are particularly interesting to you?

_____

✳ Write a letter to a friend who is going to read Le Guin in an English class. Tell your friend what you know about Le Guin and give all the advice you can about how to approach the reading of science fiction and fantasy.

_____
_____
_____
_____
_____
_____
_____
_____
_____
_____
_____
_____

How does knowing about the author's interests and reasons for writing help you to understand the larger meaning behind her stories?

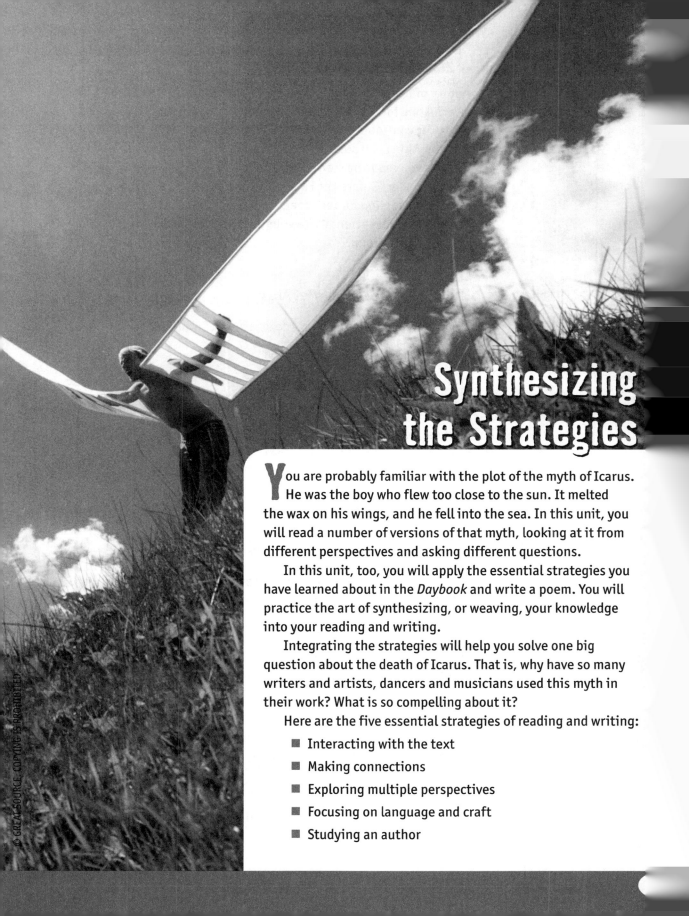

Synthesizing the Strategies

You are probably familiar with the plot of the myth of Icarus. He was the boy who flew too close to the sun. It melted the wax on his wings, and he fell into the sea. In this unit, you will read a number of versions of that myth, looking at it from different perspectives and asking different questions.

In this unit, too, you will apply the essential strategies you have learned about in the *Daybook* and write a poem. You will practice the art of synthesizing, or weaving, your knowledge into your reading and writing.

Integrating the strategies will help you solve one big question about the death of Icarus. That is, why have so many writers and artists, dancers and musicians used this myth in their work? What is so compelling about it?

Here are the five essential strategies of reading and writing:

- Interacting with the text
- Making connections
- Exploring multiple perspectives
- Focusing on language and craft
- Studying an author

The story of Icarus, which you will explore in this unit, has been a powerful one for artists, writers, and musicians throughout the ages. Even today, it continues to exert its pull on our imaginations. Share with a partner anything you already know about Icarus. Who was he? What did he do? Have you read any stories about him?

Read the poem "Before the Fall." It was written in a summer poetry-writing session for teenagers in England. Read it first without any additional explanation. Write your questions and thoughts in the **Response Notes** column.

Response Notes

Before the Fall by Harriet Archer

"He sets his mind at work upon unknown arts, and changes the laws of nature."
                                        —Ovid

The passage out of Crete is closed to all,
the coast swoops

Except those with the ability to leave
The heavy bonds of land, the draw of sea.

shrinking to a slice of yellow

With feathers, wax and string, ambition,
And Athene's guidance, is constructed,
Grafted onto shoulders, moulded weightlessness.

which swells and subsides as the spray, haze and feathers sparkle,
    bird high—

Although to flee with artificial wings,
Minoan punishment for Sicilian freedom,
Is as yet unattempted—

i could sink my fingers into the sky

—though to fly
As if we had been shaped by gods to raze

just as my toes touch the water

The emptiness between the heavens and earth . . .

in flight, limbs are empty—
eyes dissolve in brightness, lemon light

clouds dive and roar, raw heat stings

and the air around him sings
(leaping with shining water
racing, chasing the sun)

Icarus can fly—why does he need wings?

TRACKING DOWN THE MYTH

The myth of Icarus is so widespread that it seems to pop up everywhere—in stories, in poems, in paintings, in dance, in comic books, in movies. The first thing you will do in this investigation is to look at the story that is the basis for Harriet Archer's poem.

The earliest known version of the myth is in Ovid's *Metamorphoses*, although there are earlier references to it. They are found on vases and wall carvings that predate Ovid, who was born in 43 BCE. All writers since Ovid have based their versions on his. After Ovid, the best-known version is the well-known account of the fall of Icarus, told by Thomas Bulfinch in the nineteenth century. This is the basic story found in Bulfinch's collection of myths, *The Age of Fable*.

Before you read the story of Icarus as told by Thomas Bulfinch, recall what you and your partner shared about the myth prior to reading "Before the Fall." After you read each paragraph of the story, jot a little note to remind yourself of what happened. When you read your notes all together, you should be able to retell the story.

The Basic Story told by Thomas Bulfinch

Icarus was imprisoned with his father Daedalus in a tower on Crete by the king Minos. Daedalus, who was known for his creativity and inventions, figured out how to escape from the tower. He knew he could not leave the island by sea, as the king kept strict watch on all the vessels, and permitted none to sail without being carefully searched. "Minos may control the land and sea," said Daedalus, "but not the regions of the air. I will try that way." So he set to work to fabricate wings for himself and his young son Icarus. He put feathers together beginning with the smallest and adding larger, so as to form an increasing surface. The larger ones he secured with thread and the smaller with wax, and gave the whole a gentle curvature like the wings of a bird. Icarus, the boy, stood and looked on, sometimes running to gather up the feathers which the wind had blown away, and then handling the wax and working it over with his fingers, by his play impeding his father in his labors.

When at last the work was done, Daedalus the artist, waving his wings, found himself buoyed upward and hung suspended, poising himself on the updraft of air. He next fitted wings on his son's arms and shoulders in the same manner, and taught him how to fly, as a bird tempts her young ones from the lofty nest into the air. When all was prepared for flight, he said, "Icarus, my son, I charge you to keep at a moderate height, for if you fly too low the dampness will clog your wings, and plunge you into the ocean. And if you fly too high, the heat will melt them. Keep near me and you will be safe." While he gave him these instructions and fitted the wings to his shoulders, the face of the father was wet with tears, and his hands trembled. He hugged the boy, not knowing that it was for the last time. Then rising on his wings he flew off, encouraging Icarus to follow, and looked back from his own flight to see how his son managed his wings. As they flew, the plowman in the field stopped his work to gaze, and the shepherd leaned on his staff and watched them, astonished at the sight, and thinking they were gods who could thus fly like the birds through the air.

They passed small islands on the left and a larger one on the right, then the boy, exulting in his joyous flight, began to leave the guidance of his father and soar upward as if to reach heaven. The nearness of the blazing sun softened the wax which held the feathers together, and they began to fall off. He fluttered with his arms, but no feathers remained to hold the air. While his mouth uttered cries to his father, he plummeted; and the sound was submerged in the blue waters of the sea. His father cried, "Icarus, Icarus, where are you?" At last he saw the feathers floating on the water, and bitterly lamenting his own skill that had fashioned the wings, he buried the body. The sea was thenceforth called the Icarian Sea in honor of his name. And Daedalus called the land where he was buried Icaria in memory of his child. Daedalus himself arrived safely in Sicily, where he built a temple to Apollo, and hung up his wings, an offering to the god. ❖

✳ Since this version was written by Thomas Bulfinch more than a century ago, you may have found some words with which you were unfamiliar. List those words here:

Vocabulary Words   Definitions

_____   _____

_____   _____

✳ Review your lists with a partner to see whether you can figure out the meanings of these words. Write down your "working definitions" (what you think they might mean). If there are still words on your list without definitions, look them up in the dictionary. Then write the definitions of those words.

✳ Reread the story. Add any new ideas or questions you have as a result of your second reading of the story.

_____

_____

_____

✳ Reread the poem "Before the Fall" on pages 102–103. In light of the story you just read, what additional insights do you have into the poem?

_____

_____

_____

✳ What are some possible meanings of the question in the last line of the poem: *"Icarus can fly—why does he need wings?"*

_____

_____

_____

✳ What stories from your own experience remind you of the Icarus story? Explain why. Cite an example from the text.

_____

_____

_____

_____

_____

_____

Based on this introduction to the myth of Icarus, why do you think so many writers make a connection to this story?

In the poem "Ghost," poet Peter McDonald takes on the persona of Icarus. Look for words that express the poet's feelings.

Ghost by Peter McDonald

Response Notes

Held like a gull in the blue air,
outflying summer, I shall leave
the true gods of this world

for the emptiness of sky, its seasons,
a blossom of quiet clouds, the cold
store of love, fear, dreams coming true. ✦

✳ The poet imagines that he is Icarus in this poem.
- To whom do you think Icarus is speaking ? _____
- What else might Icarus say? Write three or more additional lines for the poem.

_____
_____
_____
_____

In the next poem, the poet takes the position of onlooker to Icarus's story, as first Icarus is fitted with the wings and then flies off into the sky. Notice where his fear changes to exultation.

Icarus by Lyman Andrews

Icarus, his hair
crackling like thunder,
stood first on one leg
then on the other,
trembling
at his father's touch
as the great wings were fitted
with strong bands of leather

across his narrow breast.
His feet quivered
and his heart jerked
with that young excitement
that leaves the bowels hollow,
until at last the wings
were on, and Daedalus stood
and said: these wings are made
for our escape; and frowned
a warning at his son
who couldn't hear a word.
Icarus plunged head down
into the shining air
and soaring, rising, diving,
he rinsed himself of those
old terrors of earth, clay
and metallic deaths:
but the sea glittered
with the strewn fragments
of the sun, and
the heat, white-hot
as new hammer-leavings,
stirred the wax to liquid
in the wings, until
the boy Icarus,
seeing feathers break-
ing free, struggled harder
and found he was not frightened
but just feeling godlike
and in that blinding moment
he made his last, noble
effort, ignored the shout
of Daedalus, and sprang
still higher, until his sweat sizzled
gashes broke red (bright coals)
through the charred crust
of his ribcage
and then
        only
                ashes
falling like blackbirds
to the waiting sea ❖

✳ Make a sketch of Icarus as you imagine Lyman Andrews sees him. Around the sketch, write words from the poem that reflect your drawing.

✳ Write a short response to these questions:
■ So far, what do the poets' views of Icarus have in common? How are they different?

_____
_____
_____
_____
_____
_____

■ How do the poets' views of Icarus echo or counter your own emerging view of Icarus?

_____
_____
_____
_____
_____

How is your view of Icarus evolving as you read?

I magine that Icarus survived the fall into the sea and now lives in a suburban area near a city, such as Los Angeles. That's what poet Edward Field imagined when he wrote this poem. Highlight parts of the poem that make you think differently about the story of Icarus.

Icarus by Edward Field

Only the feathers floating around the hat
Showed that anything more spectacular had occurred
Than the usual drowning. The police preferred to ignore
The confusing aspects of the case,
And the witnesses ran off to a gang war.
So the report filed and forgotten in the archives read simply
"Drowned," but it was wrong: Icarus
Had swum away, coming at last to the city
Where he rented a house and tended the garden.

"That nice Mr. Hicks" the neighbors called him,
Never dreaming that the gray, respectable suit
Concealed arms that had controlled huge wings
Nor that those sad, defeated eyes had once
Compelled the sun. And had he told them
they would have answered with a shocked,
uncomprehending stare.
No, he could not disturb their neat front yards;
Yet all his books insisted that this was a horrible mistake:
What was he doing aging in a suburb?
Can the genius of the hero fall
To the middling stature of the merely talented?

And nightly Icarus probes his wound
And daily in his workshop, curtains carefully drawn,
Constructs small wings and tries to fly
To the lighting fixture on the ceiling:
Fails every time and hates himself for trying.

He had thought himself a hero, had acted heroically,
And dreamt of his fall, the tragic fall of the hero;
But now rides commuter trains,
Serves on various committees,
And wishes he had drowned. ❖

✳ Discuss these questions with a partner or a group. Then use words and lines from the poem as you explain your ideas.

■ Why do you think Field's Icarus thought of himself as a hero?

■ What do you think Field means by these lines:
   "Can the genius of the hero fall
   To the middling stature of the merely talented?"

■ What might Field mean by "the tragic fall of the hero"?

■ Why, do you think, does Field's Icarus wish he had drowned?

How has your view of the
Icarus story changed by imagining
a different ending, a different
country, and a different time
in history?

In this lesson you will read two poems written by teenagers. The Icarus story has always been popular with adolescents because it shows a boy who dares to test his growing power, regardless of the consequences. In the first poem, however, the Icarus figure is a girl. Read the first poem, writing your questions and comments in the **Response Notes** column. Note, especially, the effect of using questions in the poem.

Jennifer and Icarus by Erin Keenan

Tell me, Jen,
Did anybody see you fall?
And did anybody hear you call,
If call you made, before you gave
Your body over to the grave?

Did you run, or leap, or cry,
And did you have time enough to lie
Inside, and believe that you had learnt to fly,
Or that you truly didn't care,
And allowed yourself to die?

Tell me, Jen, why?
Explain to me, Jen,
I want to understand.
They loved you and you made them cry.
Tell me then, Jennifer,
Why did that not make you fold your wings and stay? ❖

�֎ In this poem, not only time and place are changed. What else changes? How does the figure of Jennifer take on characteristics of the Icarus story?

_____

_____

_____

_____

_____

_____

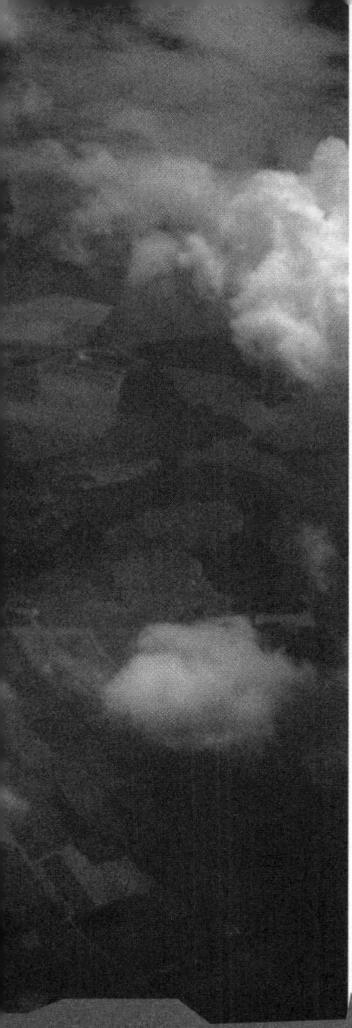

✳ Imagine a scenario in which a girl, Jennifer in this case, "folds her wings" and, like Icarus in the traditional story, dies. Write the outline of the story you imagine.

_____

_____

_____

_____

_____

_____

_____

_____

_____

_____

The next poem was written by a high school junior. He loved the Icarus story, identifying with an Icarus who was a young man living in a dream world. Read the poem; then answer the questions below.

Icarus, Come with Me by Bill Whiteman

I feel small wings
growing from my womb.
Let us walk beside the sea.
Let us taste the flesh
of freshly fallen seabirds.
Let us feel the tender oils
of Grecian mermaids.
Icarus, come with me.
The sun will never touch us
with its too many fingers
of light.
We can watch the moon
with its silent albino ponies.
Icarus, I want you
to travel with me forever.

Response Notes

I want you to come
and walk beside metal barges
that have eroded into the tide.
I want to comb your tired feathers.
Let me brush your solemn wings.
Icarus, come with me,
come with me.

My child has fallen.
His wings have melted
into summer clouds.
His eyes have grown soft
from looking at the sun too long.
His once-beautiful blonde feathers
have grown dark and dull.
Icarus, why did you try
to make love with the sun,
with its evil chariot,
with its mirrored beauty.
You should have come with me, Icarus,
I loved you. ❖

❉ Who is speaking in this poem? Is it one person or two?

_____

❉ The poet was a young man who was trying to find himself and his way
in life. How does that information affect the way you read the poem?
Write your ideas about his poem here:

_____

_____

_____

_____

_____

_____

_____

What are some ways
contemporary writers make
the story of Icarus relevant to
their lives?

The last poem in this unit was inspired by a famous painting by Pieter Brueghel. The painting is titled *Landscape with the Fall of Icarus*. If you look at the painting, you'll see that it is very hard to find any clue to this title. If you look very closely, you'll see two white legs in the water in the lower right corner. Read the poem, "Musée des Beaux Arts," and you'll understand how the poet put Brueghel's perspective of Icarus into words.

Musée des Beaux Arts by W. H. Auden

Response Notes

About suffering they were never wrong,
The old Masters: how well they understood
Its human position; how it takes place
While someone else is eating or opening a window or just walking
    dully along;
How, when the aged are reverently, passionately waiting
For the miraculous birth, there always must be
Children who did not specially want it to happen, skating
On a pond at the edge of the wood:
They never forgot
That even the dreadful martyrdom must run its course
anyhow in a corner, some untidy spot

Where the dogs go on with their doggy life and the torturer's horse
Scratches its innocent behind on a tree.

In Breughel's Icarus, for instance: how everything turns away
Quite leisurely from the disaster; the ploughman may
Have heard the splash, the forsaken cry,
But for him it was not an important failure; the sun shone
As it had to on the white legs disappearing into the green
Water; and the expensive delicate ship that must have seen
Something amazing, a boy falling out of the sky,
Had somewhere to get to and sailed calmly on. ⟴

❋ This is the most famous poem that derives from the story of Icarus as
shown by the painting by Brueghel. Read the poem again. Try to find
correspondences to parts of the painting.

■ Why do you think Brueghel titled the painting *Landscape with the
Fall of Icarus* when all you see of Icarus is two white legs in the
corner of the painting?

_____

_____

_____

_____

_____

■ What do you think Auden was saying about human nature in the
face of tragedy? Cite examples from the text to support your answer.

_____

_____

_____

_____

_____

_____

_____

_____

You have now read many versions of the Icarus story as told by Bulfinch: "Ghost" by Peter McDonald, "Icarus" by Lyman Andrews, "Icarus" by Edward Field, "Musée Des Beaux Arts" by W. H. Auden, and three poems by teenagers ("Before The Fall" by Harriet Archer, "Icarus, Come with Me" by Bill Whiteman, and "Jennifer and Icarus" by Erin Keenan).

❋ Think about possible story lines you might develop in a poem using the Icarus story as a starting point. For example, what if the father of your friend designed a racing car for his son, and his son died in a fiery crash? Think about some possible instances of teenagers behaving recklessly against the wishes of their parents. On the other hand, perhaps you wish to show the story of Icarus flying toward the sun as an exultant, free-wheeling, joyous flight. What might such an Icarus be thinking?

❋ Choose a scenario and jot down ideas for your own poem.

❋ Use this space to jot down your ideas. Then use your own paper to write a poem on the theme of the flight and fall of Icarus.

After your exploration of the death of Icarus, why do you think this story is still such a rich source of inspiration for songwriters, poets, and other artists today?

Deepening Your Investigation

Recall something you created—a sculpture, a meal, a song, a poem, or a drawing, for example. What did you learn from creating it? Now imagine that you are going to create something similar, but you want to make it even better. How can you draw on the knowledge, skills, and strategies you used the first time?

Throughout the *Daybook,* you have been asked to use reading strategies will help you build and enrich your understanding of what you read. You are probably becoming more skillful at using strategies that help you grow as a reader. In this unit, you will use the essential strategies to expand your investigation into myths of human flight that are related to the Icarus myth. Through reading remarkable tales of flying and writing your own tale, you will work to deepen your understanding of the myths of flight while developing five essential reading strategies:

- Interacting with the text
- Making connections
- Exploring multiple perspectives
- Focusing on language and craft
- Studying an author

In earlier lessons in this *Daybook,* you practiced many ways of **interacting with the text** as you read. Take a moment to list some of those strategies in the left column of the chart below.

INTERACTING WITH THE TEXT

Strategies I have been using	Other strategies I will try

■ Share your list with a partner. If you have questions about how your partner uses a particular strategy, ask for clarification and an example. Generate a list of strategies with one other pair of students.

■ Now take a moment to fill in the right column of your chart. List strategies for interacting with the text that you have not been using when you read. You may use ideas that you got from your partner or what you learned from the other pair of students.

What do you think the myths of flight convey? As you interact with the ideas in the folktale "The People Could Fly," record your thoughts about this question in the **Response Notes.**

from **The People Could Fly** by Virginia Hamilton

They say the people could fly. Say that long ago in Africa, some of the people knew magic. And they would walk up on the air like climbin up on a gate. And they flew like blackbirds over the fields. Black, shiny wings flappin against the blue up there.

Then, many of the people were captured for Slavery. The ones that could fly shed their wings. They couldn't take their wings across the water on the slave ships. Too crowded, don't you know.

The folks were full of misery, then. Got sick with the up and down of the sea. So they forgot about flyin when they could no longer breathe the sweet scent of Africa.

Say the people who could fly kept their power, although they shed their wings. They kept their secret magic in the land of slavery. They looked the same as the other people from Africa who had been coming over, who had dark skin. Say you couldn't tell anymore one who *could fly from one who couldn't.*

✳ One way to interact with the text is to *imagine* what might happen in the folktale. Do you have this strategy on your list? Share with a partner ideas you have about what might happen in "The People Could Fly." Then write the next part of the tale. Try to use a voice and language consistent with an oral folktale, such as Virginia Hamilton's.

_____

_____

_____

_____

_____

_____

_____

_____

_____

✳ Read the excerpt on page 120, which presents another aspect of the flying myths. Remember to use the **Response Notes** column to try various ways of interacting with the text.

Response Notes

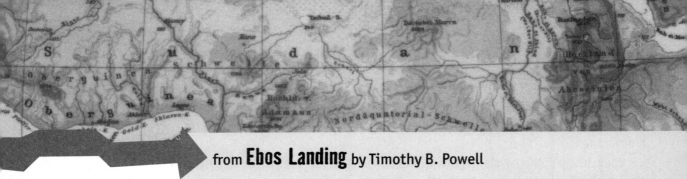

from **Ebos Landing** by Timothy B. Powell

[The "Myth of the Flying Africans"] has been told and embellished for 200 years in the form of local legends, children's stories, movies, novels, and television shows. Based on an actual historical event, this remarkable tale of an Ebo (or Igbo) slave rebellion on St. Simons Island has become a powerful metaphor of African American courage, longing, and conviction.

The historical roots of the flying Africans legend can be traced back to the spring of 1803, when a group of Igbo slaves arrived in Savannah after enduring the nightmare of the Middle Passage. The Igbo (from what is now the nation of Nigeria, in central West Africa) were renowned throughout the American South for being fiercely independent and unwilling to tolerate the humiliations of chattel slavery. The Igbo who became known as the flying Africans were purchased at the slave market in Savannah by agents working on behalf of John Couper and Thomas Spalding. Loaded aboard a small vessel, the Igbo were confined below deck for the trip down the coast to St. Simons. During the course of the journey, however, the Igbo rose up in rebellion against the white agents, who jumped overboard and were drowned.

What happened next is a striking example of the ways in which African American slaves and white slave masters interpreted "history" in starkly different terms. One of the only contemporary written accounts of the event was by Roswell King, a white overseer on the nearby plantation of Pierce Butler. King recounted that as soon as the Igbo landed on St. Simons Island, they "took to the swamp"—committing suicide by walking into Dunbar Creek. . . .

African American oral tradition, on the other hand, has preserved a very different account of the events that transpired that day. As with all oral histories, the facts of the story have evolved as storytellers elaborated the tale over the years, such that there are now dozens of variations on the original episode. In the late 1930s, more than 100 years after the Igbo uprising on St. Simons, members of the Federal Writers Project collected oral histories in the Sea Islands (many of which can now be found in *Drums and Shadows: Survival Studies among the Georgia Coastal Negroes*). An older African American man by the name of Wallace Quarterman was asked if he had heard the story of Ebos landing. Quarterman replied:

Ain't you heard about them? Well, at that time Mr. Blue he was the overseer and . . . Mr. Blue he go down one morning with a long whip for to whip them good. . . . Anyway, he whipped them good and they got together and stuck that hoe in the field and then . . . rose up in the sky and turned themselves into buzzards and flew right back to Africa. . . . Everybody knows about them.

This account of transforming the hardships of slavery into the magical powers of freedom has been retold by a distinguished array of African American artists throughout the last century. . . .

. . . By transforming the painful memories of slavery and racism into the emancipating power of flight, the story of the flying Africans continues to play an important role in maintaining a cultural connection to Africa and empowering generations of black Americans. ❖

❋ Another way to interact with the text is to develop a thoughtful response to what you read. Write about your reactions to the explanations provided in *Ebos Landing*. What questions do the explanations raise for you about how and when people choose to create mythic stories? How effective are the stories?

_____

_____

_____

_____

_____

_____

_____

_____

_____

_____

_____

_____

_____

_____

_____

_____

_____

What did you learn about African tales of flight? Which strategies for interacting with the text helped you reach these understandings?

When you read a story that engages you, you make many different kinds of **connections.** For example, as you read the flying African stories, did you make connections to the Icarus myth in Unit 7? Making connections—relating a story to yourself or to other people, events, and places, or stories—helps you create deeper meaning in your reading.

Think about all the different kinds of connections you make as you read. List them in the left column of the chart below.

MAKING CONNECTIONS

Strategies I have been using	Other strategies I will try

- Compare your list with your original partner's list. Compare with another pair. Add to your "I will try" list other types of connections that your partner or another group used.

The following is a retelling of the folktale about flying Africans. As you read, record in your **Response Notes** the *personal, text, or world* connections you make.

Response Notes

All God's Chillen Had Wings by Langston Hughes and Arna Bontemps, as told by Caesar Grant of John's Island

Once all Africans could fly like birds; but owing to their many transgressions, their wings were taken away. There remained, here and there, in the sea islands and out-of-the-way places in the low country, some who had been overlooked, and had retained the power of flight, though they looked like other men.

There was a cruel master on one of the sea islands who worked his people till they died. When they died he bought others to take their places. These also he killed with overwork in the burning summer sun, through the middle hours of the day, although this was against the law.

One day, when all the worn-out Negroes were dead of overwork, he bought, of a broker in the town, a company of native Africans just brought into the country, and put them at once to work in the cottonfield.

He drove them hard. They went to work at sunrise and did not stop until dark. They were driven with unsparing harshness all day long, men, women and children. There was no pause for rest during the unendurable heat of the midsummer noon, though trees were plenty and near. But through the hardest hours, when fair plantations gave their Negroes rest, this man's driver pushed the work along without a moment's stop for breath, until all grew weak with heat and thirst.

There was among them one young woman who had lately borne a child. It was her first; she had not fully recovered from bearing, and should not have been sent to the field until her strength had come back. She had her child with her, as the other women had, astraddle on her hip, or piggyback.

The baby cried. She spoke to quiet it. The driver could not understand her word. She took her breast with her hand and threw it over her shoulder that the child might suck and be content. Then she went back to chopping knot-grass; but being very weak, and sick with the great heat, she stumbled, slipped and fell.

The driver struck her with his lash until she rose and staggered on.

She spoke to an old man near her, the oldest man of them all, tall and strong, with a forked beard. He replied; but the driver could not understand what they said; their talk was strange to him.

She returned to work; but in a little while she fell again. Again the driver lashed her until she got to her feet. Again she spoke to the old man. But he said: "Not yet, daughter; not yet." So she went on working, though she was very ill.

Soon she stumbled and fell again. But when the driver came running with his lash to drive her on with her work, she turned to the old man and asked: "Is it time yet, daddy?" He answered: "Yes, daughter; the time has come. Go; and peace be with you!" . . . and stretched out his arms toward her . . . so.

With that she leaped straight up into the air and was gone like a bird, flying over field and wood.

The driver and overseer ran after her as far as the edge of the field; but she was gone, high over their heads, over the fence, and over the top of the woods, gone, with her baby astraddle of her hip, sucking at her breast. ❖

❊ Look over your **Response Notes.** Which types of connections do you tend to make most often? Discuss them with a partner.

Response Notes

Then the driver hurried the rest to make up for her loss; and the sun was very hot indeed. So hot that soon a man fell down. The overseer himself lashed him to his feet. As he got up from where he had fallen the old man called to him in an unknown tongue. My grandfather told me the words that he said; but it was a long time ago, and I have forgotten them. But when he had spoken, the man turned and laughed at the overseer, and leaped up into the air, and was gone, like a gull, flying over field and wood.

Soon after another man fell. The driver lashed him. He turned to the old man. The old man cried out to him, and stretched out his arms as he had done for the other two; and he, like them, leaped up, and was gone through the air, flying like a bird over field and wood.

Then the overseer cried to the driver, and the master cried to them both: "Beat the old devil! He is the doer!"

The overseer and the driver ran at the old man with lashes ready; and the master ran too, with a picket pulled from the fence, to beat the life out of the old man who had made those Negroes fly.

But the old man laughed in their faces, and said something loudly to all the Negroes in the field, the new Negroes and the old Negroes.

And as he spoke to them they all remembered what they had forgotten, and recalled the power which once had been theirs. Then all the Negroes, old and new, stood up together; the old man raised his hands; and they all leaped up into the air with a great shout; and in a moment were gone, flying, like a flock of crows, over the field, over the fence, and over the top of the wood; and behind them flew the old man.

The men went clapping their hands; and the women went singing; and those who had children gave them their breasts; and the children laughed and sucked as their mothers flew, and were not afraid.

The master, the overseer, and the driver looked after them as they flew, beyond the wood, beyond the river, miles on miles, until they passed beyond the last rim of the world and disappeared in the sky like a handful of leaves. They were never seen again.

Where they went I do not know; I never was told. Nor what it was that the old man said . . . that I have forgotten. But as he went over the last fence he made a sign in the master's face, and cried "Kuli-ba! Kuli-ba!" I don't know what that means.

But if I could only find the old wood sawyer, he could tell you more; for he was there at the time, and saw the Africans fly away with their women and children. He is an old, old man, over ninety years of age, and remembers a great many strange things. ❖

✳ Recalling all the myths of flight that you have read so far in Units 7 and 8, write a short essay in which you offer your conclusions about the significance of stories of human flight. Provide specific examples from your reading. Reveal something of yourself to help your reader understand why you react as you do.

_____

_____

_____

_____

_____

_____

_____

_____

_____

_____

_____

_____

_____

_____

_____

_____

_____

_____

_____

_____

_____

What do your connections between the stories of human flight suggest to you about why this myth is told across different cultures, times, and places?

EXPLORING MULTIPLE PERSPECTIVES

One way to practice **exploring multiple perspectives** is to put yourself in the shoes of several different characters in a story. In this way, you attempt to understand each character's perspective—*what* each character sees and *how* and *why* the character sees it that way. This can be challenging to do, particularly if you do not feel you relate to or sympathize with a character. However, exploring multiple perspectives can also help you develop multiple interpretations of a story. By putting yourself in others' shoes you gain a deeper understanding not only of what you read, but also of the world around you.

The tale of the flying Africans depicts people drawing forth a special power to break free from slavery—to rise up from brutal oppression. In the following excerpt from a memoir, the author relates a tale her grandfather told about a woman who went flying during the night. From what might the flying woman in this tale be trying to break free? Consider that question as you read the tale, which is told in the third person. Record your thoughts in the **Response Notes** column.

Response Notes

from **Black Ice** by Lorene Cary

. . . I began to tell myself Pap's old stories. They began in the black night, too.

"Can you imagine how black? With not a light anywhere. So black and dark that women were sure to be home by nightfall, because they didn't know what could be out there..."

. . . I imagined that the spirits were always women, like the one who slipped out of her skin at night and flew around in the darkness. She left her skin draped over a chair by the window, as easily as others leave their lingerie. When her husband realized what was happening, he went to an old woman in the village and asked how he could keep his wife home with him, where she belonged. The old woman told him to pretend to be asleep that night and wait until his wife was gone. Then he was to take salt and rub it on the inside of her skin. So he did. Just before the following dawn, when the sky began to lighten a little, but the moon still shone white and silver through the window, the husband heard the rustling and then a shriek of pain as the wife tried to slip back in. "Skin, skin," she screamed, "ya no know me?"❖

✳ What is your first interpretation of the story? How do you explain what happened?

_____

_____

_____

_____

✳ Now consider the tale from the perspective of the flying woman by imagining that you are that woman. Rewrite the tale in the first person. Include some of her thoughts about why she chooses to fly, why she must leave her skin behind, and how the skin makes her feel.

_____

_____

_____

_____

_____

_____

_____

✳ Imagine that you are the husband. Rewrite the tale in the first person. Have him narrate the story. Include his thoughts on why he feels the need to keep his wife at home or how he felt when she screamed out in pain from the salt.

_____

_____

_____

_____

_____

_____

✳ The versions of the tale you wrote from the different perspectives illustrate your interpretations of the story. Share your retellings with a partner, and discuss the differences and similarities.

How does examining the perspectives of multiple characters influence your interpretation of a story?

FOCUSING ON LANGUAGE AND CRAFT

How do language and craft enhance a reader's experience? It is important to pay attention to the words an author uses and the ways those words are arranged. There are many strategies you can use to understand the words and the structure of what you read. Some of them are

- focusing on the author's word choice;
- looking at the way the author uses words;
- examining how the author puts words together to form meaningful phrases;
- understanding figurative language;
- comparing the author's style with other writers' styles.

Examine how one poet, Robert Hayden, uses the Icarus myth to tell the story of African American dreams of flight. In your **Response Notes,** comment specifically on language choice and other elements of craft that you notice.

Response Notes

O Daedalus, Fly Away Home by Robert Hayden

Drifting night in the Georgia pines,
coonskin drum and jubilee banjo.
    Pretty Malinda, dance with me.

Night is juba, night is conjo.
    Pretty Malinda, dance with me.

Night is an African juju man
weaving a wish and a weariness together
    to make two wings.

    O fly away home fly away

Do you remember Africa?

    O cleave the air fly away home

My gran, he flew back to Africa,
just spread his arms and
    flew away home.

Drifting night in the windy pines;
night is a laughing, night is a longing.
    Pretty Malinda, come to me.

Night is a mourning juju man
weaving a wish and a weariness together
   to make two wings.

   O fly away home fly away

❋ Rereading the poem and using your **Response Notes**, work with a
   partner to fill in the chart below. The chart will help you examine
   and understand words, phrases, or lines that recreate the experience
   of the poem.

LANGUAGE AND CRAFT CHART

Word, phrase, or line	Your interpretation/What you think it means	What it makes you think, see, or feel

Robert Hayden often wrote about the African American experience, using
many different forms for his poems. The poem on page 130, about escaped
slave and prominent abolitionist Frederick Douglass, is written in the form
of a **sonnet.** This type of sonnet consists of fourteen lines. A sonnet usually
begins with an idea, question, or challenge, which is resolved or brought to
a conclusion at the end of the poem. Some believe that sonnets mirror the
way we think about difficult ideas, with pauses or interruptions as we work
our way to a conclusion. Sonnets often deal with love or other challenging
philosophical issues.

❋ As you read Hayden's sonnet about Frederick Douglass, consider
   the poem's meaning, as well as the way it was written. Record your
   thoughts in your **Response Notes.**

Frederick Douglass by Robert Hayden

When it is finally ours, this freedom, this liberty, this beautiful
and terrible thing, needful to man as air,
usable as earth; when it belongs at last to all,
when it is truly instinct, brain matter, diastole, systole,
reflex action; when it is finally won; when it is more
than the gaudy mumbo jumbo of politicians:
this man, this Douglass, this former slave, this Negro
beaten to his knees, exiled, visioning a world
where none is lonely, none hunted, alien,
this man, superb in love and logic, this man
shall be remembered. Oh, not with statues' rhetoric,
not with legends and poems and wreaths of bronze alone,
but with the lives grown out of his life, the lives
fleshing his dream of the beautiful, needful thing.

✳ Write own version of the flight myth in a poem or narrative. For
example, are there times you'd like to take flight? Are there ways to
do so? What are the advantages and consequences of taking flight?
Revisit the myths to borrow words, phrases, and ideas.

_____

_____

_____

_____

_____

_____

_____

_____

What are some ways that
language and craft are used in
the various myths of flight? How
do these emphasize different
meanings of the myth?

 Share your draft with a partner.

You can often gain insight into a writer's work by learning some background about the writer's life. Not all works are autobiographical, but many authors draw on their experiences and beliefs when they write. To understand the myths of flight more fully, biographical insights present another angle for understanding the particular perspective of a writer. The following strategies will help you do that.

- Making inferences about the connections between the author's life and work
- Noticing the author's subject matter and sources of inspiration
- Paying attention to repeated themes and topics
- Reading what an author says about his or her own work and what critics say

from Collected Poems: Robert Hayden
by Arnold Rampersad

Response Notes

As an individual, Hayden was a man subjected virtually from the start of his life to harsh personal pressures that might easily have silenced someone less courageous. His work is further testimony to the power of the artist to find and illuminate the profoundly human in the midst of chaos, and to produce art as a bulwark against the will to inhumanity that is such an essential part of the human condition.

Robert Earl Hayden was born in Detroit, Michigan, on August 4, 1913, the son of Asa and Ruth Sheffey. His parents named him Asa Bundy Sheffey. Before he was two, however, their marriage collapsed and his mother, traveling in search of work, gave him up to a poor but respectable couple in the neighborhood, William and Sue Ellen Hayden. Although the child remained aware of the identity of his natural parents, saw them from time to time, and eventually became close once again with his mother, he grew up as a foster child of the Haydens, who renamed him and reared him as their son. He would discover only when he was forty, by accident, that they had never adopted him legally or even officially changed his name, although they had led him to believe that they had done both. His adoptive father, a laborer who sometimes had trouble finding work, was a disciplinarian and dedicated Baptist. His adoptive mother, according to the Hayden scholar Pontheolla Taylor Williams, "regaled Robert with Afro-American folktales, stories of southern racial atrocities, and her own post-Civil War experiences, when she was a chambermaid on Ohio River steamers."

... His experience of racial difference was bittersweet. Hayden passed his earliest years in a section of Detroit (later nicknamed Paradise Valley) that remained racially diverse until an influx of Southern blacks in search of jobs, followed by reactive white flight, turned it virtually all-black. His early familiarity with Jews, Germans, Italians, and other whites, reflected in several of his poems, perhaps laid the foundation for the transracial philosophy that is a hallmark of Hayden's art. Attending a mainly white high school, he felt both a degree of ostracism and, at the same time, a degree of acceptance and understanding support.

Hayden's myopia [an eye condition that required him to wear very thick glasses] and the cruelty it often inspired drove him inward and toward books, where he soon discovered the particular solace of poetry. Midway through his teenage years he already knew the most popular of the modern writers, including whites such as Edna St. Vincent Millay and Carl Sandburg and blacks such as Langston Hughes and Countee Cullen. He was especially taken with the example of Countee Cullen, whose emotional and lyrical blending of race consciousness with traditional poetics left an immediate mark on Hayden's youthful writing." ❖

✳ Taking what you have learned about Hayden into account, why do you think the flight myth might have some significance for him? Give specific evidence from his poem and biography that lead you to your speculations.

How does knowing something about the author help you to better understand the purpose and significance of the author's work?

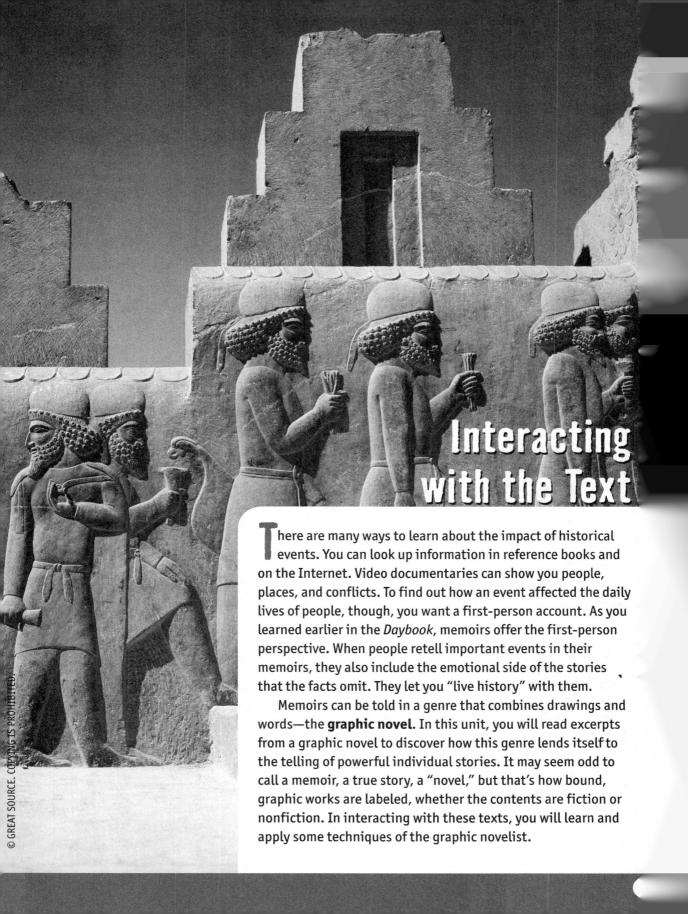

Interacting with the Text

There are many ways to learn about the impact of historical events. You can look up information in reference books and on the Internet. Video documentaries can show you people, places, and conflicts. To find out how an event affected the daily lives of people, though, you want a first-person account. As you learned earlier in the *Daybook*, memoirs offer the first-person perspective. When people retell important events in their memoirs, they also include the emotional side of the stories that the facts omit. They let you "live history" with them.

Memoirs can be told in a genre that combines drawings and words—the **graphic novel**. In this unit, you will read excerpts from a graphic novel to discover how this genre lends itself to the telling of powerful individual stories. It may seem odd to call a memoir, a true story, a "novel," but that's how bound, graphic works are labeled, whether the contents are fiction or nonfiction. In interacting with these texts, you will learn and apply some techniques of the graphic novelist.

For many people, a **graphic novel** is a new form. Others may be accustomed to reading stories that combine pictures and words, but people in both groups can benefit from learning about this form. A person who wants to create something—a videogame, a car, a poem—is likely to examine what others have done. They do this, not to copy, but to understand the limits and extend the possibilities of the form they have chosen to use. **Interacting with the text** by taking note of the form can expand your understanding of both the form and the content.

As you read the first part of "The Veil," from the memoir *Persepolis*, write questions and make observations about the story and the graphic novel structure on and around the excerpt.

from **The Veil** in *Persepolis* by Marjane Satrapi

THIS IS ME WHEN I WAS 10 YEARS OLD. THIS WAS IN 1980.

AND THIS IS A CLASS PHOTO. I'M SITTING ON THE FAR LEFT SO YOU DON'T SEE ME. FROM LEFT TO RIGHT: GOLNAZ, MAHSHID, NARINE, MINNA.

IN 1979 A REVOLUTION TOOK PLACE. IT WAS LATER CALLED "THE ISLAMIC REVOLUTION".

THEN CAME 1980: THE YEAR IT BECAME OBLIGATORY TO WEAR THE VEIL AT SCHOOL.

WEAR THIS !

This panel is bigger than the others.

✳ Discuss your observations and questions with a partner. Then answer these questions.

■ Look at the rounded word balloons and the rectangular blocks of words. Who is speaking in the rectangles? What impact do these sentences have on the reader?

_____

_____

_____

_____

_____

_____

■ What does the background (black or white) for each panel suggest to you about the author's opinion of the events?

_____

_____

_____

_____

_____

_____

How do your observations expand your understanding of the form and content?

ome graphic novelists, such as Marjane Satrapi, use different shapes and sizes for the panels that tell the story. These panels and the spaces between them help writers present their story the way they want. Review the previous lesson to form hypotheses about why different shapes are used. The four shapes that repeat appear in the first three rows of panels. The story opens with a vertical rectangle, followed by a medium horizontal rectangle. In the next row are two squares. The third row is one wide horizontal rectangle.

✳ In the box below, write two speculations about how Satrapi decides to use certain panel shapes in particular combinations.

✳ Graphic novelists also use the *gutter*, or the space between panels, to help them tell their story. Because our minds automatically fill gaps in the story, using the gutter can be an effective way to convey more information in a compact form. For example, between the first two panels, there is no gap in time. The first panel is connected to the second one with a repeated detail—part of the speaker's veil. Between the third and fourth panel, though, a year has elapsed. Why do you suppose Satrapi chose to present the sequence of events this way?

✳ As you read the next part of "The Veil," see if your hypotheses about the shapes of panels are confirmed. Also, consider how the spaces between the panels help tell the story.

from **The Veil** in *Persepolis* by Marjane Satrapi

EVERYWHERE IN THE STREETS THERE WERE DEMONSTRATIONS FOR AND AGAINST THE VEIL.

the veil! the veil! the veil! the veil! the veil!

freedom! freedom! freedom! freedom! freedom!

AT ONE OF THE DEMONSTRATIONS, A GERMAN JOURNALIST TOOK A PHOTO OF MY MOTHER.

I WAS REALLY PROUD OF HER. HER PHOTO WAS PUBLISHED IN ALL THE EUROPEAN NEWSPAPERS.

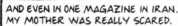

AND EVEN IN ONE MAGAZINE IN IRAN, MY MOTHER WAS REALLY SCARED.

HAVE YOU SEEN THIS?

DON'T WORRY, DARLING.

SHE DYED HER HAIR,

AND WORE DARK GLASSES FOR A LONG TIME.

✳ Use the two parts of "The Veil" that you have read to write a paragraph or two explaining how Marjane Satrapi uses the shapes of the panels and the spaces between them to tell her story. Imagine that you are explaining how to understand this story to someone who has never read a graphic novel.

_____

_____

_____

_____

_____

_____

_____

_____

_____

_____

_____

_____

_____

How does focusing on the structure of the story affect your understanding of it?

Another way to interact with a text is to **build a context** for it. It could be helpful for you to find out about the history and events that are part of Satrapi's story of growing up during the Islamic Revolution in Iran. Some of the context might be contained within the story itself. Look carefully at the two panels that follow where Satrapi gives background for the revolution. Write comments or questions about the drawings.

from **The Bicycle** in *Persepolis* by Marjane Satrapi

FOLLOWED BY THE MONGOLIAN INVASION FROM THE EAST.

AND FINALLY MODERN IMPERIALISM.

❋ Briefly restate the history of Iran that Satrapi presents in these panels. Retell in words what happened.

_____

_____

❋ In the excerpts you have read, Marjane Satrapi uses the veil as a symbol of the changes that occurred after the 1979 revolution. The actions and decisions of the Shah of Iran had angered many people, including a substantial number of Moslems. Ultimately, the government of the Shah was overthrown and a religious leader took over. What do you need to know to better understand the events of 1979 and 1980? What do you already know? Take a few minutes to organize your knowledge and questions using a K-W-L chart.

What I KNOW	What I WONDER	Where I Might LEARN It

✳ Compare charts in a small group. After your discussion, add new knowledge and questions to your charts.

✳ Read the following summary from an online reference. In the **Response Notes,** mark places where you find out something you wondered about. Jot down questions that arise from the reading, too.

from Islamic Revolution of Iran in Encarta

Rule of the Shah and Rise of Khomeini

In 1963 the shah began a series of social, economic, and political reforms known as the White Revolution. The revolution gave more freedom to women and increased secular education at the expense of religious education. These and other changes questioned the dominant role of Iran's religious leaders, most of whom feared losing power and moral authority under the White Revolution. Throughout the 1970s the shah continued to anger traditional Shia Muslims, who formed a large proportion of the population. For example, the shah held festivals in 1971 to celebrate the 2500th anniversary of the pre-Islamic Persian Empire; this was perceived as a direct rebuke to the millions of Iranians who viewed the coming of Islam in the 7th century as the founding date of modern Iran.

Other sectors of the population were also becoming disenchanted with the shah. Students and intellectuals were frustrated by his autocratic rule and by the corruption of the royal family, who had become wealthy from their five decades in power. Many of these dissidents favored some form of democracy as well as a more equitable distribution of the country's income. Members of the traditional middle class, or *bazaaris,* were angry as well, because they had received little benefit from either the White Revolution's development schemes or from the country's rapid, oil-fed growth in the 1970s. Most of the earnings had instead gone to larger companies, especially to ones with international ties or connections to the shah's family. Both bazaaris and fundamentalist Muslims disapproved of Iran's growing ties with the West.

All of these factors contributed to the rise of Ruhollah Khomeini, who in the early 1960s was a relatively unknown Islamic ayatollah, or holy man. Khomeini had several assets that other leaders lacked. First, he was seemingly fearless: In 1963 he was the only cleric to openly attack the shah's White Revolution. Second, he spoke the language of the people, condemning the shah's "injustices" in the name of the "downtrodden" masses. Third, and most importantly, Khomeini was able to transform Shia Islam into a mass ideology that appealed to many groups. In the past, Shia leaders had argued that although Shia Muslims were a righteous minority who suffered under cruel leaders, it was not their role to overthrow the ruling regime and create an Islamic state. Instead, Shia clerics should defend the religion and await the return of the 12th imam, the messianic figure of Shiism whose presence was needed for the establishment of an Islamic state. Khomeini, however, rejected this passive approach. He argued that by overthrowing the shah, Iranians would hasten the return of the 12th imam. Indeed, Khomeini did not discourage Iranians from thinking of him as the messianic imam. Khomeini spread his alluring mixture of revolutionary ideology and messianic revivalism by mobilizing a vast network of loyal disciples. He was also able to galvanize the support of the bazaari middle class, which had close links to the *ulema,* Iran's religious leaders.

In 1964 the shah exiled Khomeini from Iran. Khomeini eventually settled in the Iraqi holy city of An Najaf, from which he broadcast his messages to his Iranian followers. In 1978 the Iraqi government, fearful that the ayatollah's powerful message would create similar disturbances in Iraq, expelled Khomeini. He then went to France, from which he sent audio tapes of his revolutionary message to Iran.

The Revolution

In 1978 opponents of the shah had several bloody encounters with his security troops. The most notorious of these clashes was on September 8, when soldiers fired on 20,000 demonstrators in Tehran. Several hundred people were killed and thousands more were wounded in what became known as Black Friday. Two months later, young people took to the streets of Tehran, burning shops, banks, liquor stores, and other symbols of Western "corruption." Tensions escalated in December with the coming of Muharram, the sacred month marking the martyrdom of Husayn, an early Shia leader. Emboldened by the strength of the opposition, Khomeini called on Iranians to "begin the month of epic heroism the month in which the leader of the Muslims taught us to struggle against all tyrants." On December 10 and 11, the two holiest days of the Shia calendar, a group of soldiers rebelled and attacked the officer's mess of the shah's Imperial Guard. With that, his regime collapsed, and the shah fled Iran in January 1979. He died two years later in Cairo, Egypt.

Khomeini returned to Iran on February 1, 1979, and began to establish control over the government. He forced the shah's prime minister out of office and appointed a new prime minister, Mehdi Bazargan. Bazargan was known as a liberal who favored democracy, so many observers believed the new government would represent a wide range of opinion. In a late March referendum Iranians voted on a new form of government, and in April, with overwhelming public approval, Khomeini declared the establishment of the Islamic Republic of Iran.

In November 1979, after the shah had been allowed entry to the United States for medical care, hundreds of Iranians overran the U.S. embassy in Tehran and took the staff hostage. Khomeini refused to release them until the United States apologized for its support of the shah and met other demands. (The hostages were eventually released in January 1981 after Ronald Reagan replaced Jimmy Carter as president.). Khomeini used the fervor of the hostage taking to mobilize radical Islamic students against Bazargan. After Bazargan resigned, Khomeini held a December referendum in which more than 99 percent of voters supported a new constitution. Khomeini became *faqih,* or ultimate leader, and used his unlimited powers to eliminate opponents. First he attacked liberals and leftists, including President Abolhassan Bani-Sadr, who fled Iran in February 1981; later, he repressed his clerical opponents. By 1981 some 1600 people had been executed under Khomeini. ❖

What are the advantages and disadvantages of presenting information in graphic novel form?

❉ Return to the K-W-L chart on page 141 and add information from your reading. What do you know now? What do you wonder about now?

When you **interact with the text,** you also interact with the author. Even if you cannot personally talk with the author, you might wonder how the author's writing connects with his or her experiences, as well as your own. As you read what Marjane Satrapi says about why she wrote *Persepolis,* think about the parts of the book you have read. Use the **Response Notes** to write about the connections you see.

On Writing *Persepolis* by Marjane Satrapi

Response Notes

Why I Wrote *Persepolis*

From the time I came to France in 1994, I was always telling stories about life in Iran to my friends. We'd see pieces about Iran on television, but they didn't represent my experience at all. I had to keep saying, "No, it's not like that there." I've been justifying why it isn't negative to be Iranian for almost twenty years. How strange when it isn't something I did or chose to be?

After I finished university, there were nine of us, all artists and friends, working in a studio together. That group finally said, "Do something with your stories." They introduced me to graphic novelists. . . .

Writing a Graphic Novel Is Like Making a Movie

People always ask me, "Why didn't you write a book?" But that's what *Persepolis* is. To me, a book is pages related to something that has a cover. Graphic novels are not traditional literature, but that does not mean they are second-rate. Images are a way of writing. When you have the talent to be able to write and to draw it seems a shame to choose one. I think it's better to do both.

We learn about the world through images all the time. In the cinema we do it, but to make a film you need sponsors and money and 10,000 people to work with you. With a graphic novel, all you need is yourself and your editor.

Of course, you have to have a very visual vision of the world. You have to perceive life with images; otherwise it doesn't work. Some artists are more into sound; they make music. The point is that you have to know what you want to say, and find the best way of saying it. It's hard to say how *Persepolis* evolved once I started writing. I had to learn how to write it as a graphic novel by doing.

What I Wanted to Say

I'm a pacifist. I believe there are ways to solve the world's problems. Instead of putting all this money to create arms, I think countries should invest in scholarships for kids to study abroad. Perhaps they could become good and

knowledgeable professors in their own countries. You need time for that kind of changes, though.

I have been brought up open-minded. If I didn't know any people from other countries, I'd think everyone was evil based on news stories. But I know a lot of people, and know that there is no such thing as stark good and evil. Isn't it possible there is the same amount of evil everywhere?

If people are given the chance to experience life in more than one country, they will hate a little less. It's not a miracle potion, but little by little you can solve problems in the basement of a country, not on the surface. That is why I wanted people in other countries to read *Persepolis*, to see that I grew up just like other children. ❖

✳ What would you ask Marjane Satrapi if you could talk to her? What do you think she would answer? Ask questions and then try to imagine— based on everything you have read so far—how she would answer them. Write both the questions and the answers in the space below.

_____

_____

_____

_____

_____

_____

_____

_____

_____

_____

_____

_____

_____

_____

_____

In what ways does knowing the author's purpose for writing influence the way you read the text?

Marjane Satrapi says, "We learn about the world through images all the time." She used her book to create a world for readers who were not familiar with Iran. In this lesson, you have the opportunity to create images for your own purposes. Would you like to tell a story? Persuade readers to believe the same way you do about a topic? Learn about the world? Use the following chart to list some topics you might use.

SUBJECT CHART

Points I could make	What I could learn about the world
A story I could tell	**Impressions I would like to change**

 Tell a partner more about the most interesting topics from your chart. Together or separately select a topic that you could use. In the space below, identify your topic and tell what your purpose will be in creating images for it.

_____

_____

_____

_____

Use the following space to draft your graphic text. If you need more panels than you have space for, sketch them here as thumbnails (small sketches) and create a final draft on your own paper.

How does your purpose affect the techniques you use and the images you create?

Making Connections

Some stories seem inextricably tied to their time and place, while others have a timeless quality. What characteristics make some stories so timeless that generation after generation enjoys them? If the endurance of fairy tales is an indication, it may be that, as the authors of a collection of fairy tales explain, "underneath their fanciful trappings, the old tales had a lot to say about human nature: about cruelty, vanity, greed, despair—and about the 'magic' that overcomes them: kindness, compassion, generosity, faith, persistence, and courage." And perhaps, as another writer said, "Sometimes we need to have the truth exaggerated and made more dramatic, even fantastic, in order to comprehend it."

Timeless tales have the ability to stimulate countless **connections** in readers and writers. They spin a web of associations between lives real and fanciful and settings old and new. In this unit, you will make your own connections as you read four tales derived from classic fairy tales.

Some people have grown up hearing and reading many fairy tales, while others may recall only a few popular titles. Chances are, however, no matter where you grew up, you probably heard at least a few fairy tales.

Reflect on your own experiences with fairy tales. Do you have a special memory about learning a particular tale? Did you have a favorite fairy tale growing up? Can you think of a fairy tale that has influenced your thinking? Take a moment to write about your personal **connections** to fairy tales.

_____

_____

_____

_____

_____

_____

_____

_____

_____

* Now list all of the fairy tales you can think of.

_____   _____

_____   _____

_____   _____

_____   _____

_____   _____

_____   _____

_____   _____

* Share your list with a partner. If there are fairy tales on your list that your partner does not know, briefly tell the tale. Add to your list if your partner reminds you of other tales you know.

* Is the story of Little Red Riding Hood on your list? Talk with your partner about this tale. If neither of you know or remember the tale, find a pair that is discussing it. Listen in on their discussion.

Most classic fairy tales are set long ago, yet the themes in fairy tales make them timeless. Because of this, classic fairy tales lend themselves to being retold in many different ways. The new version may be a **retelling** in which the original story is set in the present day. The story may have the same plot, or it may have new, modern twists. Read the following excerpt of a modern retelling of the classic fairy tale "Little Red Riding Hood." As you read, note the **connections** you make between this retelling and the original story.

from Little Red and the Big Bad by Will Shetterly

You know I'm giving the straight and deep 'cause it's about a friend of a friend. A few weeks back, just 'cross town, a true sweet chiquita, called Red for her fave red hoodie, gets a 911 from her momma's momma. The Grams is bedbound with a winter bug, but she's jonesing for Sesame Noodles, Hot and Sour Soup, and Kung Pao Tofu from the local Chineserie—'cept their delivery wheels broke down. So Grams is notioning if Red fetches food, they'll feast together.

Red greenlights that. Veggie Asian chow and the Grams are solid in her top ten. So Red puts on her hoodie, leaves a note for the Moms, and BMXes away.

Now, down by the corner is a fine looking beastie boy who thinks he's the Big Bad, and maybe he is. He sees Red exit the eatery with a humongous bag of munch matter and calls, "Hey, Little Red Hoodie Hottie. Got me a tasty treat?"

Red doesn't slow. She just says, "Not if you're not my Grams, and you're not."

This Big Bad wouldn't be so big or so bad if he quit easy. He smiles and follows Red to her chained-up wheels. While Red juggles dinner and digs for her bike lock key, the Bad says, "Take five? Or all ten?" and holds out both hands.

Red warms to his style and his smile—this beastie boy isn't half as smooth as he thinks he is, but half is twice as smooth as this town's seen. Red hands off the bag, the Bad peeps in, and his stomach makes a five-two Richter. He's thinking he's holding the appetizer, and Red's the main course. ❖

Response Notes

Red Riding Hood wore a hooded cape.

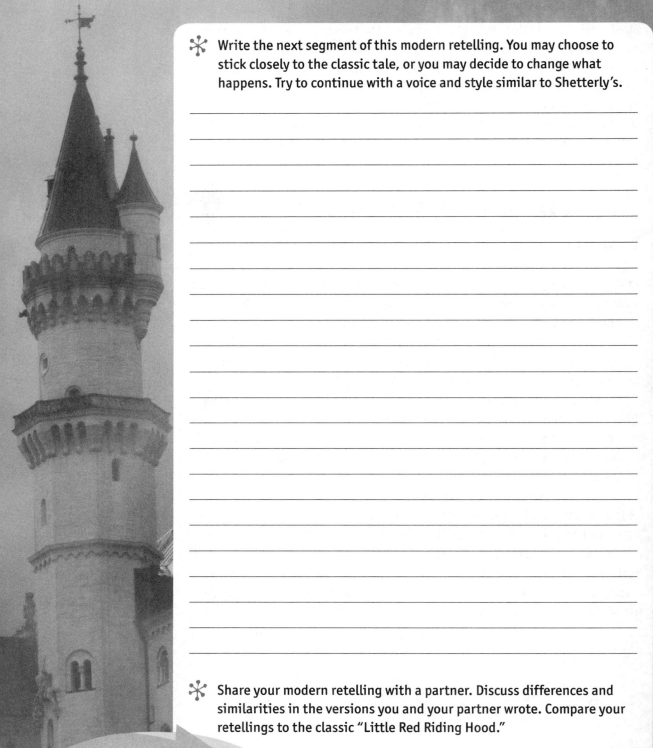

✳ Write the next segment of this modern retelling. You may choose to stick closely to the classic tale, or you may decide to change what happens. Try to continue with a voice and style similar to Shetterly's.

_____

_____

_____

_____

_____

_____

_____

_____

_____

_____

_____

_____

_____

_____

_____

_____

_____

_____

_____

_____

✳ Share your modern retelling with a partner. Discuss differences and similarities in the versions you and your partner wrote. Compare your retellings to the classic "Little Red Riding Hood."

Why do writers retell classic fairy tales? How do connections with the original stories add to the meaning of the retold tale?

Fairy tales know few cultural barriers. Sometimes stories developed in different places independently of one another, yet are surprisingly similar. In other cases, different cultures adapted fairy tales that originated elsewhere but kept the same characters and plot. And other times, the stories changed or evolved into dramatically different stories. For instance, the story upon which Cinderella is based is thought to have been first written over a thousand years ago in China. The basic plot and themes remained the same, but some elements are quite different. The source of the **protagonist's** transformation, for example—a fairy godmother in the Western tale of Cinderella and a golden fish in the Chinese tale—differs.

The following story, *Lon Po Po: A Red-Riding Hood Story from China*, is a Chinese version of "Little Red Riding Hood." In Chinese, Lon Po Po means "Grandma Wolf." As you read, pay particular attention to similarities and differences between this tale and the version you know.

from Lon Po Po: A Red-Riding Hood Story from China
by Ed Young

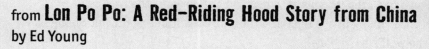

Response Notes

Once, long ago, there was a woman who lived alone in the country with her three children, Shang, Tao, and Paotze. On the day of their grandmother's birthday, the good mother set off to see her, leaving the three children at home.

Before she left, she said, "Be good while I am away, my heart-loving children; I will not return tonight. Remember to close the door tight at sunset and latch it well."

But an old wolf lived nearby and saw the good mother leave. At dusk, disguised as an old woman, he came up to the house of the children and knocked on the door twice: bang, bang.

Shang, who was the eldest, said through the latched door, "Who is it?"

"My little jewels," said the wolf, "this is your grandmother, your Po Po."

"Po Po!" Shang said. "Our mother has gone to visit you!"

The wolf acted surprised. "To visit me? I have not met her along the way. She must have taken a different route."

"Po Po!" Shang said. "How is it that you come so late?"

The wolf answered, "The journey is long, my children, and the day is short."

Shang listened through the door. "Po Po," she said, "why is your voice so low?"

"Your grandmother has caught a cold, good children, and it is dark and windy out here. Quickly open up, and let your Po Po come in," the cunning wolf said.

© GREAT SOURCE. COPYING IS PROHIBITED.

Tao and Paotze could not wait. One unlatched the door and the other opened it. They shouted, "Po Po, Po Po, come in!"

At the moment he entered the door, the wolf blew out the candle.

"Po Po," Shang asked, "why did you blow out the candle? The room is now dark."

The wolf did not answer.

Tao and Paotze rushed to their Po Po and wished to be hugged. The old wolf held Tao. "Good child, you are so plump." He embraced Paotze. "Good child, you have grown to be so sweet."

Soon the old wolf pretended to be sleepy. He yawned. "All the chicks are in the coop," he said. "Po Po is sleepy too." When he climbed into the big bed, Paotze climbed in at one end with the wolf, and Shang and Tao climbed in at the other.

But when Shang stretched, she touched the wolf's tail. "Po Po, Po Po, your foot has a bush on it."

"Po Po has brought hemp strings to weave you a basket," the wolf said.

Shang touched grandmother's sharp claws. "Po Po, Po Po, your hand has thorns on it."

"Po Po has brought an awl to make shoes for you," the wolf said.

At once, Shang lit the light and the wolf blew it out again, but Shang had seen the wolf's hairy face.

"Po Po, Po Po," she said, for she was not only the eldest, she was the most clever, "you must be hungry. Have you eaten gingko nuts?"

"What is gingko?" the wolf asked.

"Gingko is soft and tender, like the skin of a baby. One taste and you will live forever," Shang said, "and the nuts grow on the top of the tree just outside the door."

The wolf gave a sigh. "Oh, dear. Po Po is old, her bones have become brittle. No longer can she climb trees."

"Good Po Po, we can pick some for you," Shang said.

The wolf was delighted.

Shang jumped out of bed and Tao and Paotze came with her to the gingko tree. There, Shang told her sisters about the wolf and all three climbed up the tall tree. ❖

✳ Fill in the chart on the next page, indicating the similarities and differences between "Little Red and the Big Bad," *Lon Po Po*, and the classic "Little Red Riding Hood." Be sure to include a comparison of characters, plot, theme, and other elements you noticed.

Similarities		Differences
_____	**"Little Red Riding Hood"**	_____
_____		_____
_____		_____
_____	*Lon Po Po*	_____
_____		_____
_____		_____
_____	**"Little Red and the Big Bad"**	_____

✳ What is the most significant similarity between the three tales?

_____

_____

_____

✳ What is the most significant difference?

_____

_____

_____

✳ One way to make connections is to analyze comparisons. Using your responses, as well as your chart, write the opening paragraph of an essay that will compare the three versions of "Little Red Riding Hood. "

_____

_____

_____

_____

_____

_____

_____

_____

How does making connections between different versions of "Little Red Riding Hood" emphasize the meaning of the basic story?

Many stories are loosely based on or inspired by classic fairy tales. The following retelling, also derived from "Little Red Riding Hood," retains a setting similar to the classic tale, but significantly reconstructs the plot. Read the beginning of "Lupe" by Kathe Koja. In your **Response Notes,** record the **connections** you make with other versions you have read.

Lupe by Kathe Koja

Do you ever go into the woods? Not the park, always so dusty-dirty, torn paper wrappers and splintery seesaws, four old trees leaned up like broken boards against the fence. No, I mean the *woods,* the place where the town's noise fades away as if there is no town at all; where the trees stand like an army, where the bears and wild pigs live, and Old Blanca the witch, the place all the grandmammas say *Stay away from!*

In the woods everything is different. The light slants different, like underwater; the grass is sharp and pointy with morning frost. And the smells— a hundred scents, a thousand every second: dead-leaf spice and bitterroot, mold and rot and berry, I couldn't guess or name them all but they don't need names, they just are: like the trees, the needle frost, the slanting light: and me.

Response Notes

✳ Discuss with your partner the major differences between other Red Riding Hood stories and this one so far.

As the story continues, we learn that the narrator, Lupe, had a baby brother named Teodoro, who lived only a short time. When he died, everyone in the family handled it differently. Her Papa carved countless "mamma-and-baby" figurines out of wood. Her brother 'Nando got into lots of fights. Her Mamma "walked around the house like a ghost, hardly eating" or sleeping. Lupe spent time in the woods by herself, until one day her family found out.

As you continue reading the story, jot in your **Response Notes** connections you make, especially to other fairy tales and stories.

"The woods," ['Nando] called. "That's where Lupe goes. Carlos and Aimi told me, they said she goes there every day."

Papa came all the way out now, frowning lines in the sawdust mask. In his hand was another mamma-and-baby, just born from the ragged wood. "The woods, Lupe? What do you do there?"

I sit and watch the trees, Papa, and the squirrels dancing like falling leaves. I listen to the sounds that are so small you can hardly hear them.

I look for wolf tracks. I drink water from the stream I found. I think of Teodoro. "Nothing," I said.

"Nothing," hollow, like an echo from right behind me, so close I jumped—but it was Mamma, her hair hanging down like black seaweed, her eyes red. "Nothing she does all day, lazy girl. Why don't you help your mamma? Poor Mamma, there's no one for her now."

Papa clutched the mamma-and-baby. 'Nando edged closer to the door. None of us spoke. Mamma squeezed my arm; her hand was damp and hot, as if she had a fever, like Teodoro. "I'll help you," I said. My voice sounded strange, as if I were far away. I wished I were far away, back in the woods, so far inside no one could find me. "What do you want me to do?"

"Go into the woods for me," Mamma said. "Go and see Old Blanca."

Papa's lips went tight; he set the wooden people down. "No, Maria," he said, hands on Mamma's forearms, his face close to hers as if he would kiss her, as if they were alone in the room. "That's no errand for a child. Old Blanca is—"

"A *bruja!*" 'Nando shouted. "She eats children, she's a witch!"

Mamma wrenched away from him, her eyes redder now, an awful red; they made me think of the wild boar, fierce and tusking, blind to everything but hunger. "Who else can help me? Who else will give me back what I have lost?"

"Maria, no! Maria—"

"I'll go," I said; I had to say it twice to make them hear. "I know the way, Mamma, I'll go to Old Blanca for you."

Her mother packed a basket of things: scraps of cloth, wheat cakes, grapes, and one of Papa's half-made mamma-and-baby carvings. Papa handed her a knife to keep in her pocket. Lupe set out into the woods, scared, yet brave.

With one arm, I tugged at the tangled brush, searching for the door; the basket handle dug into my arm as I knocked, one, two, firm with my fist and "Excuse me!" I called—and scared myself, my voice sounded so loud in the quiet. "Excuse me, Grandmother Blanca, I have something for you!"

No answer, only the faraway bird sounds, the brooding quiet of the hut. Something rustled behind me, a stealthy sound. I turned fast, the scraping knife snatched from my pocket—but no one was there.

Heart pounding, I knocked again, more firmly this time. Maybe she was sleeping inside; maybe she had turned herself into a spider with tiny little ears. "*Abuela* Blanca! Please, my mamma needs you!" ❖

✳ What happens next may differ significantly from the classic tale. Lupe, the "Red Riding Hood," may not get eaten by a wolf, hunters may not save her or her family, and it's possible that there is no happy-ever-after ending. What are some alternate story lines you can imagine? Note your ideas here.

_____

_____

_____

_____

_____

_____

✳ Share your ideas with a partner. Discuss how each idea relates to the theme of the story or the message it conveys.

✳ In your opinion, which version of the Little Red Riding Hood story is most successful? Explain.

_____

_____

_____

_____

_____

_____

_____

_____

_____

_____

Why do you think writers use classic stories as their inspiration? How do they create connections that cause their readers to think about the earlier versions of the story?

_____

_____

Have you ever finished a movie or a story and asked yourself, "I wonder what happens now to those characters"? With fictional stories, what happens next to the characters is entirely conceived within your imagination. In the following excerpt, Gregory Maguire imagines how the seven dwarves in the Snow White fairy tale felt after she went off with the prince. The result is an epilogue—a piece of writing that attempts to bring closure to a story that concluded with loose ends.

- Before reading the selection, discuss the classic fairy tale "Snow White and the Seven Dwarves" with a small group of classmates.

- In the **Response Notes** column, record similarities and differences that you notice between this text and the original Snow White story.

from **The Seven Stage a Comeback** by Gregory Maguire

1. So that's how it is, fellows.
    The man with the crazed expression
    Clawed open her coffin,
    Kissed her awake,
    And carried her off.
    There goes our lovely daughter.
    All (we) have left of her
    Is the apple that tumbled from her lips
    And the glass box we nested her in.

2. We're better off without her.
    I always told you that.
    And you, and you, and you two, too.
    (*You*, I rarely spoke to. Mop up your nose.")
    Wasn't she always on us about something?
    "Can't you tidy the woodpile some?"
    "Hasn't anyone ever heard of a thing called soap?"
    "I don't trust little men with beards."
    And then with the sighs.
    The expressive eyes.
    Followed by floods of agitated song.
    Frankly, when she ate that poisoned apple—
    Oh, yes, I was sad, I cried—
    But you want to know what else?
    I thought: *At last. A little peace and quiet around here.* ▶

Response Notes

This version is told by the dwarves.

3. So why are your eyes all rimmed with red?
   You loved her as we all did.
   Her with her lips like October apples,
   Her hair like the wind on April nights.
   Or did you just like having someone to complain about?
   You kept your vigil as I did. As we all did.

4. And all that's left is the apple and the coffin.
   The fruit and the glass.
   And our troubled hearts.
   Let's worry a solution out of this.
   What could we do?
   Put the bit of the apple in the glass coffin
   And close it up again?
   The coffin keeps things pretty fresh.
   And for a good, long time, too, it seems.
   You never know when we'll need a bit of poison apple again.

   . . .

1. So listen, guys. Put down your beer steins.
   Life hasn't been kind to us.
   We find an orphan girl, we take her in.
   Locate some moldy blankets to keep her warm.
   Porridge in the morning, porridge in the evening.
   A little dwarf folk music to cheer her up.
   It was a humble life, but it was ours,
   And freely we gave it to her.
   No wonder we're still upset.
   No wonder we can't focus.
   On our plates, our gray beard hardens.
   In the cold cauldron, our soup grows a skin of scum.
   We have to shape up. We're falling to pieces here.

2. Easy come, easy go.
   We're better off without her.
   Remember, I always said that.

3. You are the one who speaks with the sharpest tongue,
   But you're the one who moans her name in your sleep.
   Face it. We all miss her.
   When's the last time any one of us laughed out loud?
   Sorrow has a name, and its name is loneliness.
   Sorrow has a shape, and its shape is absence.
   Sorrow is a sickness like any other.
   We don't manage to do what we should.
   We never go out with our iron-head hammer

To bash the jewels out of secret caves.
Our hearts are bashed instead.
But what can we do?

4. We could go find her where she is.
   We could beg her to come back.
   We could bring the glass coffin.
   We could lay her where she was.

5. Let's take the coffin on our backs
   And wander o'er the mountain tracks.
   Sing ho! for the life of a dwarf.

6. Please, would you stop your singing, please?
   It's hard to think.
   Though I'm not one for kidnapping old friends,
   She did leave us high and dry.
   She married that traveling prince.
   They could be nine kingdoms away by now.
   It has been months already.
   I doubt we could ever find her.
   But I'm a one for putting on boots
   And marching impressively right off a cliff.
   Better than sitting around with tears in our beards! ❖

✳ What do you imagine might happen next? Write the rest of the tale.
Try to follow the form and style of the author, Gregory Maguire.

_____

_____

_____

_____

_____

_____

✳ Read your tale aloud to a partner.
Discuss how it is similar to and
different from "Snow White." What
do those similarities and differences
suggest about your feelings toward
the classic tale?

How does
reading and writing
an epilogue affect the
way you make connections
to "Snow White"?

You have read several derivations of classic fairy tales, and you have written the endings to a few as well. In this lesson, you will write your own retelling of a fairytale. First, read the following excerpt about the history of fairy tales. As you read, consider which fairy tale you would like to use as your foundation story.

from **Swan Sister: Fairy Tales Retold** edited by Ellen Datlow and Terri Windling

When we were kids, we were told that fairy tales were only for little children—which implies, of course, that we'd lose our interest as we grew up. But we kept on reading fairy tales year after year, and they were just as wonderful as ever. Was there something wrong with us, we wondered, that we were so enchanted by nursery stories? And why, we wondered, were fairy tales considered suitable for little children anyway? Some of the stories we read in the Brothers Grimm volumes seemed grim indeed! There were queens who danced to death in red-hot shoes, wicked witches burned up in ovens, ghostly children weeping blood red tears, and wolves lurking in Granny's nightclothes.

Eventually we learned that in previous centuries fairy tales weren't considered *children's* stories—back then, they were told to everyone, young and old alike. But in the nineteenth and twentieth centuries, certain book editors, as well as the Walt Disney Studios, took hold of fairy tales and *changed* them. They turned harrowing, suspenseful stories into sweet and simple tales full of frolicking bluebirds, giggling mice, square-jawed heroes, and dumb-blonde princesses. In these new versions of fairy tales the Good were always unambiguously Good, and they always triumphed over Evil. Real life, however, is more complex than that. The old fairy tales were more complex than that too. Underneath their fanciful trappings, the old tales had a lot to say about human nature: about cruelty, vanity, greed, despair—and about the "magic" that overcomes them: kindness, compassion, generosity, faith, persistence, and courage.

Back in the seventeenth-century France [sic] there was a group of writers in Paris who loved those older, complex stories. And so they made it into a game, as they sat together in their elegant salons, to retell traditional fairy tales in clever, interesting new ways. In fact, some of the tales we love best today are versions first told in French salons, such as Charles Perrault's "Cinderella," complete with fairy godmother and rats turned into coachmen. Sometimes two writers would choose the same tale, and each would rewrite it in his or her own way— and then the other *salonnières* would decide who'd done it best. Today, three hundred years later, many of us still love playing this game—trying to discover fresh new ways to retell beloved old stories. ❖

✳ To prepare for writing your own version of a classic fairy tale, answer the following questions.

1 What fairy tale do you want to retell, and why?

_____

_____

_____

_____

2 In your retelling, what do you want to emphasize, and why?

_____

_____

_____

_____

3 Will you keep the same plot, or will you change what happens?

_____

_____

_____

_____

4 Where will the story take place? Describe the setting.

_____

_____

_____

_____

5 Will you keep the same characters? If not, describe your new characters.

_____

_____

_____

_____

_____

✳ Using your preliminary responses, write a draft of your story. You may choose to write it in prose, like the first selections in the unit, or you may choose to write it as a poem, like the epilogue to "Snow White and the Seven Dwarves."

_____

_____

_____

_____

_____

_____

_____

_____

_____

_____

_____

_____

_____

_____

_____

_____

_____

_____

_____

_____

_____

_____

✳ Share your story with two partners. Discuss the similarities and differences between your tale and the original version.

How does retelling a story help you to better understand and appreciate the original version?

Exploring Multiple Perspectives

How a story is told can be as important as *what* it's about. Think about a film you have seen that was adapted from a book that you liked. Did the film leave out scenes from the book that you thought were important? Did the film help you see aspects of the characters that you had not noticed when reading the book? Did you agree with the filmmaker's casting choices for the lead roles?

This unit is an inquiry into **genre.** The focus is on how the impact of content changes when the content is presented in a different form. Critical readers know that the genre of a text influences a reader's expectations of the content. We might expect, for example, that a poem will use compressed language to convey an impression or an emotion. We might expect that a news story, on the other hand, will offer facts objectively. To explore relationships between form and content, you will read **nonfiction and poetry**, in this unit, and you will experiment with genre in your writing.

READING NONFICTION

Readers expect **nonfiction** to be true. And, it mostly is. But some forms of nonfiction are more **objective** than others. We expect newspaper articles to be objective and report facts. Feature articles might give opinions supported by facts and anecdotes. Film and video producers may add incidents and characters that were not in the original event to make a better story. There are different levels of objectivity in different kinds of nonfiction.

Objectivity and subjectivity are determined, in part, by the writer's involvement in the events and by what he or she chooses to tell. As you read the following selection about bullying, use the **Response Notes** column to ask questions and to comment on the degree of objectivity you see in the article.

Response Notes

from Helping Girls Combat Relational Aggression
by Marina Skowronski, et al.

Introduction

Sarah considered herself to be a serious student. She had dreams of going to college and becoming a scientist. In elementary school she was close friends with the other girls in her gifted program. She looked forward to the academic challenges of junior high. But Sarah's friends from elementary school seemed to change. They started giggling about boys and clothes and MTV; they didn't want to talk about academics or going to space camp. Sarah tried to act interested in the things the other girls were talking about, but the conversations seemed really shallow to her and the other girls made fun of her when she didn't know the latest gossip about pop stars. Soon the other girls started avoiding her and making fun of her clothes and her interests. They never included her in their trips to the mall or their sleepovers, and they looked the other way when she approached them in the lunchroom. They got boys in the class to call and pretend to ask Sarah out on dates. They even posted unflattering pictures of Sarah on the Internet. Sarah had become a victim of female relational aggression.

The term "relational aggression" describes a type of bullying primarily used by pre-adolescent and adolescent girls to victimize other girls. It is an insidious use of relationships as weapons to inflict emotional pain on others. Researchers have found that, contrary to popular belief, girls are *not* less aggressive than boys, they are just more subtle in their use of aggression. Mary Pipher, a clinical psychologist, focused attention on this form of harassment through her best-selling book, *Reviving Ophelia*. She notes that relational aggression is not a new social problem, but it is one that is becoming more widely recognized.

Knowing that your child is the victim of any act of bullying can be devastating to a parent. Understanding the nature of relational aggression can help detect harassment and help children learn to respond and seek support.

Relational aggression can be devastating. Loss of friendships and social standing are psychologically damaging; the isolation and harassment can be unbearable for the victim. Girls are particularly vulnerable because of the high value they typically place on friendships. Victims sometimes feel that they are in part to blame and therefore deserve to be isolated. The isolation makes them feel socially inept and unattractive, and thus more deserving of isolation.

When their teen daughters appear sullen, secretive and moody, many parents attribute these behaviors to normal hormonal changes and adolescent rebellion; however, these may well be symptoms that the girl is a victim of relational aggression. School absences, anxiety, depression, and long-term mental health concerns can all be consequences of relational aggression.

Victims of relational aggression often experience a range of difficulties in school, where much of the harassment takes place. Seemingly harmless school activities become painful experiences. Victims may struggle to find a seat in the lunchroom, participate in team projects, work with a partner in science, or join a team in gym class. These students feel vulnerable, and the problem is invisible to school faculty. Hallways, cafeterias, buses, and locker rooms all are places that may cause anxiety. Students may become so anxious that worries about being harassed or excluded replace concern for academic achievement. In fact, it has been reported that 160,000 students each year fail to attend school out of fear of relational aggression.

At its extreme, relational aggression has been linked to acts of school violence. Researchers have described how many school shooters, boys and girls, turn to violence when they are victims of isolation and poor treatment by peers. For example, a 14-year-old from Pennsylvania shot and killed one of her female classmates. In court, the defendant's lawyer reported that the youngster shot her classmate in order to free herself from repeated incidents of teasing and verbal abuse. ❖

✳ Use the rating scale to show how objective you think this article is.

1	2	3	4	5
Completely subjective				**Completely objective**

✳ Discuss this article and your rating with a partner.

- Is the writer a participant in the facts or just reporting them?
- What seems to be the writer's opinion of relational aggression and how do you know?
- What would make the article more subjective or objective?

✳ Make this article more subjective by writing a first-person journal entry about bullying. Write it from the perspective of the person being bullied or of a relative, such as a sibling or a parent. Use facts from the article.

_____

_____

_____

_____

_____

_____

_____

_____

_____

_____

_____

To what extent does the genre affect the reader's expectation of subjectivity or objectivity of the content?

_____

_____

_____

An **autobiography** is often considered to be more **subjective** than a biography. The writer is intimately involved with the subject—himself or herself—and the story is often told with more emotion than a biography. The reader is left with not only the facts of the writer's life but also an impression of the writer's character.

The following excerpt is from *Always Running,* Luis Rodriguez's autobiography about growing up with gangs, poverty, and prejudice in Los Angeles. In the excerpt, Rodriguez talks about his relationship with Rano, the brother who was three years older than he. In the **Response Notes** column, write your impressions of Rano and of the brothers' relationship.

from **Always Running** by Luis J. Rodriguez

Although we moved around the Watts area, the house on 105th Street near McKinley Avenue held my earliest memories, my earliest fears and questions. It was a small matchbox of a place. Next to it stood a tiny garage with holes through the walls and an unpainted barnlike quality. The weather battered it into a leaning shed. The backyard was a jungle. Vegetation appeared to grow down from the sky. There were banana trees, huge "sperm" weeds (named that because they stank like semen when you cut them), foxtails and yellowed grass. An avocado tree grew in the middle of the yard and its roots covered every bit of ground, tearing up cement walks while its branches scraped the bedroom windows. A sway of clothes on some lines filled the little bit of grassy area just behind the house.

My brother and I played often in our jungle, even pretending to be Tarzan (Rano mastered the Tarzan yell from the movies). The problem, however, was I usually ended up being the monkey who got thrown off the trees. In fact, I remember my brother as the most dangerous person alive. He seemed to be wracked with a scream which never let out. His face was dark with meanness, what my mother called *maldad*. He also took delight in seeing me writhe in pain, cry or cower, vulnerable to his own inflated sense of power. This hunger for cruelty included his ability to take my mom's most wicked whippings—without crying or wincing. He'd just sit there and stare at a wall, forcing Mama to resort to other implements of pain—but Rano would not show any emotion.

Yet in the streets, neighborhood kids often chased Rano from play or jumped him. Many times he came home mangled, his face swollen. Once somebody threw a rock at him which cut a gash across his forehead, leaving a scar Rano has to this day.

Response Notes

Another time a neighbor's kid smashed a metal bucket over Rano's head, slicing the skin over his skull and creating a horrifying scene with blood everywhere. My mother in her broken English could remedy few of the injustices, but she tried. When this one happened, she ran next door to confront that kid's mother. The woman had been sitting on her porch and saw everything.

"Qué pasó aquí?" Mama asked.

"I don't know what you want," the woman said. "All I know is your boy picked up that bucket and hit himself over the head—that's all I know."

In school, they placed Rano in classes with retarded children because he didn't speak much English. They even held him back a year in the second grade.

For all this, Rano took his rage out on me. I recall hiding from him when he came around looking for a playmate. My mother actually forced me out of closets with a belt in her hand and made me play with him.

One day we were playing on the rooftop of our house.

"Grillo, come over here," he said from the roof's edge. "Man, look at this on the ground."

I should have known better, but I leaned over to see. Rano then pushed me and I struck the ground on my back with a loud thump and lost my breath, laying deathly still in suffocating agony, until I slowly gained it back.

Another time he made me the Indian to his cowboy, tossed a rope around my neck and pulled me around the yard. He stopped barely before it choked the life out of me. I had rope burns around my neck for a week. ❖

✳ Rodriguez says that Rano had a "hunger for cruelty." Circle specific words or phrases that show Rano's cruelty. Notice how the author reinforces his portrayal through repeated incidents and details.

✳ What are your impressions of Luis and Rano? How do you think the incidents in this excerpt would change if they were included in Rano's autobiography? Write a few sentences from Rano's autobiography, telling about the same incidents that Luis related.

_____

_____

_____

_____

In what ways does changing the storyteller change the impression that the reader gets?

_____

_____

_____

Good writers show more than one side of important characters. Rodriguez shifts the emphasis when he describes a significant incident in detail. Note the ways he shows another side of Rano in this excerpt by marking words and phrases in your **Response Notes.**

from **Always Running** by Luis J. Rodriguez

One day, my mother asked Rano and me to go to the grocery store. We decided to go across the railroad tracks into South Gate. In those days, South Gate was an Anglo neighborhood, filled with the families of workers from the auto plant and other nearby industry. Like Lynwood or Huntington Park, it was forbidden territory for the people of Watts.

My brother insisted we go. I don't know what possessed him, but then I never did. It was useless to argue; he'd force me anyway. He was nine then, I was six. So without ceremony, we started over the tracks, climbing over discarded market carts and torn-up sofas, across Alameda Street, into South Gate: all-white, all-American.

We entered the first small corner grocery store we found. Everything was cool at first. We bought some bread, milk, soup cans and candy. We each walked out with a bag filled with food. We barely got a few feet, though, when five teenagers on bikes approached. We tried not to pay attention and proceeded to our side of the tracks. But the youths pulled up in front of us. While two of them stood nearby on their bikes, three of them jumped off theirs and walked over to us.

"What do we got here?" one of the boys said. . . .

He pushed me to the ground; the groceries splattered onto the asphalt. I felt melted gum and chips of broken beer bottle on my lips and cheek. Then somebody picked me up and held me while the others seized my brother, tossed his groceries out, and pounded on him. They punched him in the face, in the stomach, then his face again, cutting his lip, causing him to vomit.

I remember the shrill, maddening laughter of one of the kids on a bike, this laughing like a raven's wail, a harsh wind's shriek, a laugh that I would hear in countless beatings thereafter. I watched the others take turns on my brother; this terror of a brother, and he doubled over, had blood and spew on his shirt, and tears down his face. I wanted to do something, but they held me and I just looked on, as every strike against Rano opened me up inside.

They finally let my brother go and he slid to the ground, like a rotten banana squeezed out of its peeling. They threw us back over the tracks. In the sunset I could see the Watts Towers, shimmers of seventy thousand pieces of broken bottles, sea shells, ceramic and metal on spiraling points puncturing the heavens, which reflected back the rays of a falling sun. My brother and I then picked ourselves up, saw the teenagers take off, still laughing, still talking about those stupid greasers who dared to cross over to South Gate.

Up until then my brother had never shown any emotion to me other than disdain. He had never asked me anything, unless it was a demand, an expectation, an obligation to be his throwaway boy-doll. But for this once he looked at me, tears welled in his eyes, blood streamed from several cuts—lips and cheeks swollen.

"Swear—you got to swear—you'll never tell anybody how I cried," he said.

I suppose I did promise. It was his one last thing to hang onto, his rep as someone who could take a belt whipping, who could take a beating in the neighborhood and still go back risking more—it was this pathetic plea from the pavement I remember. I must have promised. ❖

✳ Luis writes, "every strike against Rano opened me up inside." Circle in the text other details that show Luis was sympathetic toward Rano.

✳ Discuss the two excerpts from *Always Running* with a partner or a small group.

■ What are your impressions of Luis and Rano now?

■ Have your impressions changed?

■ What do you understand now about Rano's cruelty?

■ What did the writer do that affected your impression?

✳ Record notes from your conversation here.

_____

_____

_____

_____

_____

_____

_____

What tools does an author have that can change a reader's impression?

I n "'Race' Politics," Luis Rodriguez shifts genres. He presents in a different
form with a different focus the incident in which his brother was beaten.
Read the poem twice, once to get an initial impression and a second time
to annotate it in your **Response Notes** with your questions, impressions,
and responses.

"Race" Politics by Luis J. Rodriguez

My brother and I—shopping for *la jefita*—
decided to get the "good food"
over on the other side of the tracks.

We dared each other.
Laughed a little.
Thought about it.
Said, what's the big deal.
Thought about that.
Decided we were men.
not boys.
Decided we should go wherever
we damn wanted to.

Oh, my brother—now he was bad.
Tough dude. Afraid of nothing.
I was afraid of him.

So there we go,
climbing over
the iron and wood ties,
over discarded sofas and bent-up market carts,
into a place called South Gate
—all white. All-American.

We entered the forbidden
narrow line of hate,
imposed,
transposed,
supposed,
a line of power/powerlessness
full of meaning,
meaning nothing—

Response Notes

those lines that crisscross
the abdomen of this land,
that strangle you
in your days, in your nights.
When you dream.

There we were, two Mexicans,
six and nine—from Watts, no less.
Oh, this was plenty reason
to hate us.

Plenty reason to run up behind us.
Five teenagers on bikes.
Plenty reason to knock
the groceries out from our arms—
          a splattering heap of soup
          cans, bread and candy.

Plenty reason to hold me down
on the hot asphalt; melted gum
          and chips of broken
          beer bottle on my lips and cheek.

Plenty reason to get my brother
by the throat, taking turns
          punching him in the face,
          cutting his lower lip,
          punching, him vomiting.

Punching until swollen and dark blue
he slid from their grasp
like a rotten banana from its peeling.
When they had enough, they threw us back,
back to Watts, its towers shiny
across the orange-red sky.

My brother then forced me
to promise not to tell anybody
how he cried.
He forced me to swear to God,
to Jesus Christ, to our long-dead
Indian Grandmother—
keepers of our meddling souls. ❖

✳ Select one image in this poem that is especially vivid for you. Write about the connections you make to that image or explain its importance in the poem.

_____

_____

_____

_____

_____

✳ On page 176, create a cluster to illustrate your main impression of Rano in the poem. Identify one word or phrase that represents the central impression. Put that word or phrase in the center oval, and then add the details that support that word or idea. For example, a cluster for the autobiographical excerpt in Lesson 52 might focus on Rano's cruelty and look like this:

His face was "dark with meanness."

He pushed Luis off the roof.

Rano was incredibly cruel.

He never showed emotion.

✳ Imagine that a newspaper reporter saw this incident and wrote
about it. Would the reporter try to be completely objective, or would
he be sympathetic to one of the groups? Pretend you are that reporter,
and turn the details of the poem into a news story. You might start by
answering *who, what, when, where, why, and how.*

_____

_____

_____

_____

_____

_____

_____

_____

_____

_____

_____

How do different
genres provide different
views of an event?

COMPARING GENRES 55 LESSON

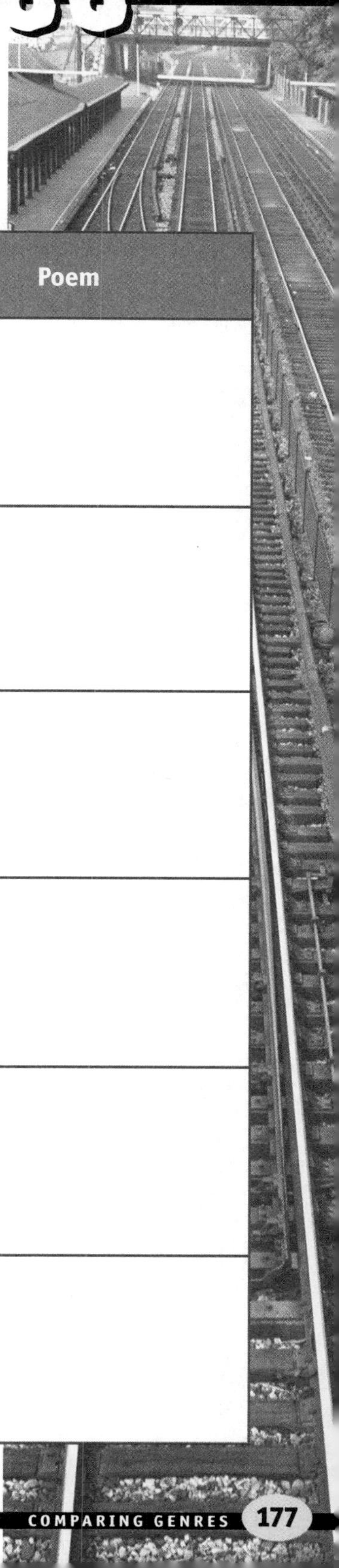

Compare the details in the two versions of the beating incident. Reread the poem and the autobiographical excerpt about the beating, and underline all the details that are similar. Use the chart below to compare the prose excerpt with the poem, filling in the blanks with details from the two selections.

Impression or focus	Prose	Poem
The relationship between Rano and Luis is complex.		
Luis feels sympathy for his brother.		
There is a focus on the issue of race relations.		
The reader can empathize with the feelings of both boys.		
The contrast between what the boys want and what they have is vivid.		
Rodriguez implies that they should not have tried to "cross the tracks."		

You have observed that the excerpts from *Always Running* and "'Race' Politics" leave different impressions. Now use the power of a shift in genre to create an impression of either Rano or the relationship between the brothers. Decide on the impression you want to create. Then find words and phrases that you can arrange into a poem of about five to eight lines. Share your poem with a partner and discuss how it is different from the autobiography.

Notes

What are the reasons a writer might decide to use the same details in works written in two different genres?

Focusing on Language and Craft

Every field has its professionals—athletes, musicians, writers, actors. Young people who want to achieve excellence in their area of interest often spend time imitating those who have already made it to the top. Artists spend time copying the works of those who have demonstrated proficiency in their fields. Writers often write and talk about how they learn their craft from imitating writers they admire. From this process, they learn techniques they can use in their own writing.

Learning from the pros is a time-tested way to improve one's skills. In this unit, you will use the work of different poets as models. **Writing from models** requires close reading. Close reading mirrors the way the brain works; it lets you get inside the author's mind. As you work with a poem, you will investigate the poet's use of language and craft so that you can learn from the pros.

"**D**id I miss anything?" Have you ever asked your teacher this question after you've missed a class? If so, you'll appreciate Tom Wayman's poem, or poetic dialogue, that begins with this question. Read the poem and try to figure out who is speaking. Is it one voice or two? Teacher and/or student? Make notes in the **Response Notes** column as you read so you'll be ready to discuss the poem.

Did I Miss Anything? by Tom Wayman

Response Notes

Question frequently asked by
students after missing a class

Nothing. When we realized you weren't here
we sat with our hands folded on our desks
in silence, for the full two hours

Everything. I gave an exam worth
40 per cent of the grade for this term
and assigned some reading due today
on which I'm about to hand out a quiz
worth 50 per cent

This is harsh!

Nothing. None of the content of this course
has value or meaning
Take as many days off as you like:
any activities we undertake as a class
I assure you will not matter either to you or me
and are without purpose

Everything. A few minutes after we began last time
a shaft of light descended and an angel
or other heavenly being appeared
and revealed to us what each woman or man must do
to attain divine wisdom in this life and
the hereafter
This is the last time the class will meet
before we disperse to bring this good news to all people
    on earth

Nothing. When you are not present
how could something significant occur?

Everything. Contained in this classroom
is a microcosm of human existence
assembled for you to query and examine and ponder
This is not the only place such an opportunity has been
   gathered

but it was one place

And you weren't here ❖

INVESTIGATE TONE

> **Tone** is the attitude a writer takes towards a subject or character:
> serious, humorous, sarcastic, ironic, satirical, tongue-in-cheek,
> solemn, objective. It's what you hear behind the words when you're
> having a conversation; it lets you know what to think about what
> is being said. In writing, the tone is conveyed through choice of
> language rather than vocal intonations.

✳ As you are reading this poem aloud (and it really needs to be heard),
   ask yourself how you know whether this writer is serious.

   ■ What clues are there to the tone of the poem?

   ■ Are all the stanzas to be read using the same tone? If not, how
      do you know?

✳ How would you characterize the speaker's tone in this poem?

INVESTIGATE AN IDEA

✳ Reread the part of the poem at the top of this page.

   ■ Who is the speaker?

   ■ What do you think of the idea expressed?

   ■ What does that part of the poem say to you about how you think
      about the classroom you are in right now?

MODEL A PRO

✳ With a partner, come up with an everyday sort of question that you hear all the time but don't really pay attention to, on the same idea as *Did I miss anything?*

✳ Write alternating stanzas, each responding to the question in opposing ways.

✳ Finally, write a conclusion that has a substantial idea.

✳ Use the space below for notes. Then make a clean copy, title the poem with the question, and sign both your names.

_____

_____

_____

_____

_____

_____

_____

_____

_____

_____

_____

_____

_____

_____

_____

_____

What are some ways you can identify the tone of a piece of writing?

✳ Share your poem with your class.

Structure is not usually the first thing you notice about a poem. It may be the first thing you respond to, however, especially if it has a definite rhythm and rhyme scheme. You may become aware of it only if you take time to investigate how structure carries meaning. Read this poem about a childhood experience once for the story line.

Digging for China by Richard Wilbur

"Far enough down is China," somebody said.
"Dig deep enough and you might see the sky
As clear as at the bottom of a well.
Except it would be real—a different sky.
Then you could burrow down until you came
To China! Oh, it's nothing like New Jersey.
There's people, trees, and houses, and all that,
But much, much different. Nothing looks the same."

I went and got the trowel out of the shed
And sweated like a coolie all that morning,
Digging a hole beside the lilac-bush,
Down on my hands and knees. It was a sort
Of praying, I suspect. I watched my hand
Dig deep and darker, and I tried and tried
To dream a place where nothing was the same.
The trowel never did break through to blue.

Before the dream could weary of itself
My eyes were tired of looking into darkness,
My sunbaked head of hanging down a hole,
I stood up in a place I had forgotten,
Blinking and staggering while the earth went round
And showed me silver barns, the fields dozing
In palls of brightness, patens growing and gone
In the tides of leaves, and the whole sky china blue.
Until I got my balance back again
All that I saw was China, China, China. ❖

✳ Now reread the poem. Pay attention not only to *what* Wilbur has to say, but also *how* he says it. Note how he structures and organizes his thoughts. Why is the first stanza mostly a quotation?

_____

_____

_____

✳ There are some vocabulary words that may cause you to stop and wonder what Wilbur means. What do you think these words mean?

trowel _____

coolie _____

palls _____

patens _____

✳ Discuss with your classmates what these words might mean in the context of Wilbur's poem.

✳ Looking again at the organization of the poem, notice that there is a story line. Fill out the following chart to see how the story progresses through the three stanzas.

Stanza 1: Comment on who the two people in the poem might be.	
Stanza 2: This is the actual incident of the poem. Comment on what happens and what the child is thinking.	
Stanza 3: Explain how the incident affects the child's perception of his or her surroundings.	

✳ Discuss your responses with a partner or with the class. Include in your discussion your own experiences of the poem "Digging for China."

✳ Think about or make up an incident that could change your perception of something familiar. Follow the structure of Wilbur's poem, and write notes for a poem of your own using the format in the chart below.

NOTES FOR YOUR POEM

Stanza 1: Imagine someone advising you to do something. What does the person say?	
Stanza 2: Recount the incident (real or imaginary). Use specific, concrete images and details.	
Stanza 3: Reflect on the incident, showing how the experience changed your perception of something familiar.	

✳ Using your chart, draft a poem about the incident that you have selected. You may illustrate it if you want.

How can you use the structure of an existing poem as a model for a poem of your own?

Think of all the different ways you can use the word *even*. Make a list and then compare it with the lists of others in your class. How many ways did you come up with?

Here is a poem that depends on the word *even* and changes its meaning *even* as you read.

Even by Nathalie Handal

Nothing is even, even this line
I am writing, even this line I am waiting in,
waiting for permission to enter
the country, the house, the room.
Nothing is even, even now
that laws have been drawn and peace
is discussed on high tables,
and even if all was said to be even
I would not believe for even I know
that nothing is even—not the trees,
the flowers, not the mountains or the shadows . . .
our nature is not even so why even try to get even
instead let us find an even better place
and call it even. ❖

✳ Try to look beyond the obvious in this simple poem to see the possibility of deeper meanings. In the chart, write your thoughts about what ideas might lie behind the lines of this poem.

Lines in the poem	What meanings might lie between them
Nothing is even, even this line.	The line looks even at first, but it may not really be.

Read this poem by Handal to see how she explores the word *rain*.

The Lives of Rain by Nathalie Handal

The old Chinese man
in the health food shop
at 98th and Broadway tells me
the rain has many lives.
I wonder if he tells everyone
the same thing or if this is something
between us, wonder if he fought any wars,
killed anyone, wonder if he ever fell in love,
lost a house, lost his accent, lost a wife or
a child in the rain, wonder if he calls for
the rain when he stirs his daily soup,
wonder what hides in his silk cloth—
rice, pictures, maybe memories of rain.
Rain, he tells me, carries rumors of the dead,
of those with suitcases and epidemics,
Rain carries the memory of droughts,
of houses gone, rain like lovers
comes and goes, like soldiers go
and sometimes return to a life
no longer standing.
The Chinese man waits for me to ask—
who really knows how many lives to come. ◆

Response Notes

✳ Explore the meanings of *rain* in the poem by drawing as many pictures as you can of the images of rain you find in the poem.

✳ Think about ways to play with the meaning of a word. Choose a word that is part of your own life and language. Write a poem that explores the different ways you can use this word.

Your word: _____

_____

_____

_____

_____

_____

_____

_____

_____

_____

_____

_____

How does a poet's choice of words affect the message?

The next poem you will read begins with a simple comparison but then develops a rather complicated, **extended metaphor.** Read "Marshall" by George Macbeth, writing your questions and comments about the metaphor in the **Response Notes** column.

Marshall by George Macbeth

It occurred to Marshall
that if he were a vegetable, he'd
be a bean. Not
one of your thin, stringy
green beans, or your

dry, marbly
Burlotti beans. No, he'd be
a broad bean,
a rich, nutritious,
meaningful bean,

alert for advantages,
inquisitive with potatoes,
mixing with every kind
and condition of vegetable,
and a good friend

to meat and lager. Yes, he'd
leap from his huge
rough pod with a loud
popping sound
into the pot: always

in hot water
and out of it with a soft
heart inside
his horny carapace. He'd
carry the whole

world's hunger on
his broad shoulders, green
with best butter
or brown with gravy. And if ▶

Response Notes

some starving Indian saw his
flesh bleeding
when the gas was turned on
or the knife went in
he'd accept the homage and prayers,
and become a god, and die like a man,

which, as things were, wasn't so easy. ❖

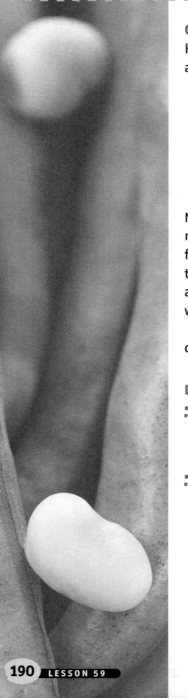

COMMENTARY FROM GEORGE MACBETH

Here's what George Macbeth said about his poem "Marshall" when asked for a brief commentary:

> It's a funny poem that turns serious, and the first of a number of rather surrealist vegetable pieces I've done—a recent sequence of twenty-four includes, for example, "The Great Crested Cucumber" and "The Vampire Marrow" (i.e., vegetables as macabre animals you wouldn't like to meet in a dark restaurant). The Aztecs, of course, thought beans were alive because they seemed to bleed to death in hot water.

Notice that the entire poem is based on a single comparison of Marshall, the main character of the poem, to a bean. Macbeth develops the metaphor by first saying what kind of bean Marshall is not and then going on to develop the kind of bean that he is. About halfway through the poem, he moves from an extended **description** of character qualities to the kinds of action he would take. ("Yes, he'd / leap from his huge rough pod . . .")

By the end of the poem, you should have a good idea of Marshall's character, conveyed through the extended metaphor of Marshall as a bean.

DISCUSSING MARSHALL AND PLANNING YOUR POEM

✳ Talk about "Marshall" with a partner or a group. Look at your annotations and raise questions and ideas that you wrote in your **Response Notes.** Then discuss the kinds of vegetables you might be.

✳ Make a list of vegetables and some of their characteristics:
- ■ What kinds of people would they be?
- ■ What would they look like as people?
- ■ What would they act like?

✳ Jot down at least two or three vegetables before you decide which one will become the basis of your poem.

Kinds of vegetables	Characteristics: descriptions and actions that this veggie-character might take

✳ Choose one of the vegetables for your poem. Give the vegetable a name. (It doesn't have to represent you, although you might want it to.) Then, following the general format of "Marshall," draft your poem. It might begin like this:

> It occurred to [the name of your character]
> that if [she/he] were a vegetable, [she'd/he'd]
> be [name of your vegetable]. Not
> one of your . . .

✳ Use this space for your notes. You may wish to work with a partner to revise it. Remember to develop your character both through description and action. Use your own paper to develop your poem.

_____

_____

_____

_____

_____

_____

_____

How can the use of metaphor enhance character development?

✳ Make a clean, edited copy of your poem when you are finished.

> In this poem, look at how the poet creates a picture of his father.
> Read "My Father After Work," by Gary Gildner, and use the **Response Notes** column to record your ideas and questions as you read.

Response Notes

My Father After Work by Gary Gildner

Putting out the candles
I think of my father asleep
on the floor beside the heat,
his work shoes side by side
on the step, his cap
capping his coat on a nail,
his socks slipping down,
and the gray hair over his ear
marked black by his pencil.

Putting out the candles
I think of winter, that quick
dark time before dinner
when he came upstairs after
shaking the furnace alive,
his cheek patched with soot,
his overalls flecked with
sawdust and snow,
and called for his pillow,
saying to wake him
when everything was ready.

Putting out the candles
I think of going away
and leaving him there,
his tanned face turning
white around the mouth,
his left hand under his head
hiding a blue nail,
the other slightly curled
at his hip, as if
the hammer had just
fallen out of it
and vanished. ❖

✳ Reread the poem, one stanza at a time. Try to visualize a picture or a symbol for each of the three stanzas. You may find your images in the words of the poem or in your own imagination as you read the words. Draw in these boxes the images or symbols that you have visualized.

Image for stanza 1	Image for stanza 2	Image for stanza 3

✳ Now draw one more image or symbol that stands for the father in the whole poem. It might be an animal that resembles the father, or it might be an object that the son identifies with him. It might be something that represents the father's personality as his son sees him.

Image for the father

EXPLAINING YOUR DRAWINGS TO A PARTNER

❋ Briefly explain why you chose the picture, image, or symbol you drew for each of the stanzas and for the father.

MODEL A PRO

❋ For the subject of your poem, choose a person who is important to you.

❋ Think of a time of day when or a place where you most often see this person.

❋ Make notes about how you could set up your poem.

❋ Each stanza follows a similar structure: the first line and the first three words of the second line are the same. Write an opening line for your poem. It should be an action that a person takes, one that happens frequently. It should be a simple act like "Opening the door" or "Listening to their conversation." Follow that line with something else that a person does. You may use Gildner's "I think . . ." if that fits, or you may choose another act.

❋ Write some possible beginnings here:

_____

_____

_____

_____

_____

_____

_____

_____

❋ Use these lines to begin each stanza. As in Gildner's poem, each stanza in your poem should describe a typical scene. Choose details that will help your readers get to know this person as you do.

❋ Use your own paper for your notes and rough draft. You may wish to work with a partner to revise. Make a clean, edited copy when you are finished.

> How has your inquiry into the use of structure and pattern helped you to write a poem about a person?

Studying an Author

Anyone who feels poetry is an alien or ominous form should consider the style in which human beings think. "How do you think?" I ask my students. "Do *you* think in complete, elaborate sentences? In fully developed paragraphs with careful footnotes? Or in flashes and bursts of images, snatches of lines leaping one to the next, descriptive fragments, sensory details?" We *think* in poetry. But some people pretend poetry is far away.

—Naomi Shihab Nye

How do *you* think? You will explore your answers to that question in this unit. **Studying an author** is one of the five essential strategies of reading and writing, a good way to get behind pieces of text. You are going to focus on one of the United States' most popular authors. You will see how all of the strategies work together to help you understand the life and work of **Naomi Shihab Nye**. You'll also get ideas about the ways *you* think.

When Bill Moyers, an investigative journalist, asked Naomi Shihab Nye in an interview, "Poetry is a form of conversation, is it not?" she responded with, "Absolutely, conversation with the world, conversation with those words on the page, allowing them to speak back to you—conversation with yourself."

The **Response Notes** you have been writing provide a way for you to have a conversation with the words in a text. In this lesson, you will go beyond the usual **Response Notes** to have a more elaborate conversation with a poem.

Read Naomi Shihab Nye's poem "The Rider," using the white space around the poem and the spaces between the lines to have a conversation with "those words on the page."

The Rider by Naomi Shihab Nye

Response Notes

A boy told me
if he roller-skated fast enough
his loneliness couldn't catch up to him,

Can you outrun loneliness?

the best reason I ever heard
for trying to be a champion.

I wonder if roller skating is a metaphor for escape.

What I wonder tonight
pedaling hard down King William Street
is if it translates to bicycles.

A victory! To leave your loneliness
panting behind you on some street corner
while you float free into a cloud of sudden azaleas,
pink petals that have never felt loneliness,
no matter how slowly they fell. ❖

✳ Read the notes you wrote around the poem. Underline words and phrases that are especially visual. If you don't find any, reread the poem, adding notes that represent pictures that come into your mind as you read.

✳ Naomi Shihab Nye imagines herself on a bicycle suddenly floating "free into a cloud of sudden azaleas." Sketch a picture of or describe in words how you might imagine yourself if you were to "float free."

✳ In this poem, Nye depicts loneliness as a living thing, a literary technique called *personification*. Find a line in the poem that shows *loneliness* acting like a person. How effective do you think this technique is? Explain.

_____

_____

_____

_____

_____

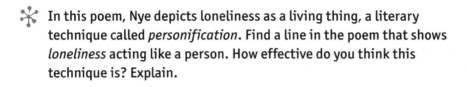

How does creating a conversation with the ideas in a text provide you with ideas of your own?

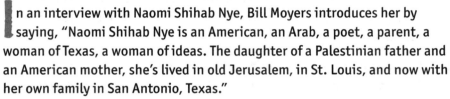

I n an interview with Naomi Shihab Nye, Bill Moyers introduces her by saying, "Naomi Shihab Nye is an American, an Arab, a poet, a parent, a woman of Texas, a woman of ideas. The daughter of a Palestinian father and an American mother, she's lived in old Jerusalem, in St. Louis, and now with her own family in San Antonio, Texas."

Naomi Shihab Nye has written many times about her grandmother, a devout Muslim who lived to be 106 years old. In all those years, she took only one trip outside of her birthplace, Palestine—that trip was to Mecca. Although Nye and her grandmother spoke different languages, there was a bond between them that Nye celebrates, not only in a number of poems, but also in a novel called *Habibi,* which means "my friend" or "sweetheart."

You will read one of Nye's poems about her grandmother. As you read, let your mind form a picture of this woman who was so important to her granddaughter. Use the **Response Notes** to record your questions, connections, images, and reflections.

Note: *Joha* is the name of a popular Jewish folklore character. He is a simpleton, innocent and stupid, a trickster, yet also appealing.

The Words Under the Words by Naomi Shihab Nye

How are "cool prayers"
soothing?

My grandmother's hands recognize grapes,
the damp shine of a goat's new skin.
When I was sick they followed me,
I woke from the long fever to find them
covering my head like cool prayers.

My grandmother's days are made of bread,
a round pat-pat and the slow baking.
She waits by the oven watching a strange car
circle the streets. Maybe it holds her son,
lost to America. More often, tourists,
who kneel and weep at mysterious shrines.
She knows how often mail arrives,
how rarely there is a letter.
When one comes, she announces it, a miracle,
listening to it read again and again
in the dim evening light.

My grandmother's voice says
nothing can surprise her.
Take her the shotgun wound and the crippled baby.
She knows the spaces we travel through,
the messages we cannot send—our voices are short
and would get lost on the journey.
Farewell to the husband's coat,
the ones she has loved and nourished,
who fly from her like seeds into a deep sky.
They will plant themselves. We will all die.

My grandmother's eyes say Allah is everywhere,
even in death.
When she talks of the orchard
and the new olive press,
when she tells the stories of Joha
and his foolish wisdoms,
He is her first thought, what she really thinks of
His name.

"Answer, if you hear the words under the words—
otherwise it is just a world
with a lot of rough edges,
difficult to get through, and our pockets
full of stones." ❖

✳ In the upper left box of the Connections and Separations chart below, record ideas from the poem that you find familiar, those with which you identify from your own family relationships. In the upper right box, record those ideas that are unfamiliar. In the lower boxes in the chart, write your ideas about the connections and separations you see in this poem.

Connections	Separations

Think about your own relationship with your grandmother or with a grandmotherly person in your life. Choose someone who is a member of your family or your extended family. (Your extended family includes people who may not be related by blood but who are an important part of your life.) If you can't think of anyone, make up a person you wish were your grandmother.

✳ Choose one of these options:

- Write something for each line, making a poem of your own.
- Choose one or two lines and continue them as a memory written in prose.

My grandmother's hands recognize_____

When I was_____

My grandmother's days are made of_____

She waits_____

She knows_____

My grandmother's voice says_____

My grandmother's eyes say_____

When she talks of_____

- When you finish, title your piece.

_____

_____

_____

_____

_____

_____

_____

_____

_____

_____

_____

_____

_____

How does connecting to the author's experiences via your own help you gain meaning from your reading?

Naomi Shihab Nye wrote a number of poems about her father, who was a grown man when he emigrated from Palestine to the United States. What kind of feelings do you think he might have about his heritage?

Read Nye's poem "Blood" and imagine what it means for her father to be an Arab. Use the **Response Notes** for your questions and thoughts.

Blood by Naomi Shihab Nye

"A true Arab knows how to catch
a fly in his hands,"
my father would say. And he'd prove it,
cupping the buzzer instantly
while the host with the swatter stared.

In the spring our palms peeled.
True Arabs believed watermelon
could heal fifty ways.
I changed these to fit the occasion.

Years before, a girl knocked,
wanted to see the Arab.
I said we didn't have one.
After that, my father told more stories
"Shihab"— "shooting star"—
a good name, borrowed from the sky.
Once I said, "When we die, we give it back?"
He said that's what a true Arab would say.

Today the headlines clot in my blood.
A Palestinian boy dangles a toy truck
on the front page.
Homeless fig, this tragedy with a terrible root
is too big for us. What flag can we wave?
I wave the flag of stone and seed,
table mat stitched in blue.

Response Notes

I call my father, we talk around the news.
It is too much for him,
neither of his two languages can reach it.
I drive into the country to find sheep, cows,
to plead with the air:
Who calls anyone *civilized*?
Where can the crying heart graze?
What does a true Arab do now?

✳ Talk with a partner about this poem. As you talk, you might ask yourselves some of these questions. Cite evidence from the poem when it's appropriate.

- What do you think Nye's father means by a "true Arab"? Do you think the father and the daughter mean the same thing by these words?

- How do you think the daughter responds to hearing about the name *Shihab*? (Notice this was her last name before she married, but she kept it as part of her name.)

- What do you think "neither of his two languages can reach it" might mean?

- What comments and questions do you and your partner still have about this poem?

_____

_____

_____

_____

_____

_____

_____

_____

_____

_____

_____

No relationship is simple. In this lesson, we will read part of the letter that Naomi Shihab Nye wrote when the author Constance Warloe asked a number of writers to write letters to their fathers.

from **The Orange, the Fig, the Whisper of Grapes**
by Naomi Shihab Nye

Dear Daddy,

All my life, from the early Mississippi River days to the steamy Texas summers, people have said you're cute, you're funny, you're adorable, what might their lives have been if they had a daddy like you? Singing in the shower in Arabic. Poking around with a shovel in the dirt, your pants rolled up. Lifting the night with your laugh. Short smart sentences. Coffee in tiny cups. Waving your hand back when you speak—as in *so what, who cares, are you kidding?* Talking to your fig tree, handing bags of ripe fruit to any Ethiopian lady who hikes down your street.

Take two, take more. Saying I love you 20 times during the same phone call. I have grown-up friends whose fathers never said that yet. Whose fathers are dead with no more chance of saying it. Your love was a solid mountain, not a hope or a guess.

You said, *The house is happy when you're in it.*

First one to say I love you in September!

Hi darling. Did you know I'm proud of you?

Rarely did you say—*Do this, don't do that*—because you were trying to figure out what to do yourself.

Let's have an orange party. Humid St. Louis evenings, savory fragrance of overturned earth in our lungs, sunstruck weeds and mown grass, you'd peel the orange skin around and around so it came off in a single springy coil, placing cool sections into our mouths. We closed our eyes for the sweetness. Somehow you and Mommy brought us up to taste a sweetness everywhere. Not to be scared.

You'd say, *This pear is AMAZING!*

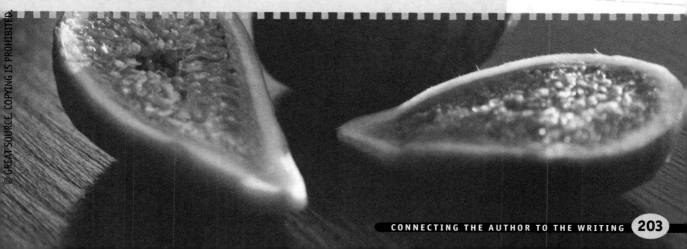

The grapevines told you a story in their own language. You translated for us. Today, the fig tree you planted in my yard, born of a single magical stick, child of your own enormous tree, towers over our clothesline. White shirts billow forth beneath it. I pinch my eyes shut, sailing to the old country of smoky stones, figs and birds.

What were you thinking of at sundown when you stood outside in the yard staring at the sky, hands locked behind your back? You grew so silent. I always imagined you making a get-away. I worried about it. You and I, the fiction-writers of the family. But I never had your endless immigrant gaze...

I found your first American drugstore in Kansas once—the archival SODA FOUNTAIN vintage. Freshly arrived at the university in that little town in 1950, you'd visit that drugstore, sit on a swivel stool at the counter, buy a Coke, and stare. An ancient druggist was in there when I went, polishing silverware with a white towel. I asked if he remembered as far back as 1950 and he pulled himself up proudly. "I remember everything since 1935! What do you want to know about any of it?"

My father. Used to sit here. At this counter. Would you possibly recall? Palestine. Jerusalem. Thick black hair. And before I could say your name, he said, "Aziz!"

The druggist held two spoons up high. "He would put his head down on the counter between sips of Coke. I thought he was either awfully tired or awfully lonely. We hardly had any foreign students here in those days. He really stood out. He didn't talk much. But I asked about his parents and the holy places. You know. Back there where he was from. He would put his head down on his arms, then lift it and stare so hard as if he could see right through that mirror over the fountain."

The mirror had clouds around the edges of it, Daddy. Your same old mirror. *First one to say I love you every day from here on out.*

Who would you see if you looked into that mirror now? ❖

Love you, Nini

✳ Imagine Nye actually sent this letter to her father. Then imagine how he would have responded. Write a letter that you think her father might have written back to her.

_____

_____

_____

_____

_____

_____

_____

_____

✳ How does your portrait of Nye's father, Aziz, develop from reading *Blood* to reading *The Orange, the Fig, the Whisper of Grapes?* List four characteristics of her father that you learned from reading *Blood*. How does the picture of the father become richer by reading the letter? List four more personal traits that developed from reading the letter.

What do I know about Aziz from *Blood?*	What do I know about Aziz from *The Orange, the Fig, the Whisper of Grapes?*

How does reading more than one text about a single subject add to or change your understanding of the subject?

In the last lesson, Naomi Shihab Nye used **imagery** in "The Orange, the Fig, the Whisper of Grapes" to evoke memories of her father. Choose one of these fruits—the orange, the fig, or the grape—and find words and phrases in her letter that connect the fruit with Nye's memory of her father. Jot them down on a sticky note or a piece of paper.

Make an outline drawing of the fruit you chose and write words and phrases from Nye's letter that connect the fruit with her memory of her father.

✳ Describe Nye's father by beginning with these words (choose one):

Aziz Shihab is like an orange because...
Aziz Shihab is like a fig because...
Aziz Shihab is like a grape because ...

✳ Read your writing to your group or to the class. Notice how each of the fruits conveys a particular aspect of Nye's father.

_____

_____

_____

_____

_____

_____

_____

_____

_____

USING IMAGERY TO DESCRIBE SOMEONE YOU KNOW

In this lesson, you have explored how a writer uses imagery to paint portraits, not just of people but also of ideas. Remember how Nye transformed *loneliness* into a person in the poem "The Rider." You have seen how she uses imagery in prose as well as in poetry.

Imagery is a primary underlying structure in language, media, and mind. It is a basic element in all aspects of language—thinking, speaking, listening, reading, and writing. When we attach to an idea an image that we see or remember, we have created a metaphor, one of the most powerful expressions of how we think and learn. The well-known linguist George Lakoff says in his book *Metaphors We Live By*, "metaphors are not simply destined for flowery prose and figurative language. On the contrary, metaphors shape the way we think and behave."

 Choose someone important in your life about whom you wish to write either a poem or a short prose piece.

- How might you go about creating a metaphor for this person? Recall how Nye used the orange, the fig, and the grape to create pictures of her father.

- What images come to your mind when you think of this person? Consider aspects of the person such as the following:
  * how he or she looks
  * how he or she acts
  * what he or she likes to do

- Decide whether you want to write a poem or a prose piece.

- Think about what structure you will use to present the person.

- What idea might you use as the finale for your piece?

✳ Use the space below to make notes or cluster your ideas before you begin to write. Draft your piece on your own paper. After revising and editing your writing, share the finished copy with your group or the class. You might want to make a beautiful copy of your piece, add illustrations, and give it as a gift to the person about whom you wrote.

_____

_____

_____

_____

_____

_____

_____

_____

_____

_____

_____

_____

_____

_____

_____

_____

_____

_____

_____

_____

_____

_____

_____

How does the author's use of craft (metaphor) influence the reader?

"While to most of us the skin is not immediately identifiable as an organ system, it is in fact the largest organ of the body. We typically think of organs as delicate internal machines performing vital functions with the skin as the outer coat, similar to the shell of a car housing the engine. However, the skin is our vital link to the outside world and its proper functioning is critical to our interaction with our environment."

Yale Health Care News, March 2000

"Skin is our largest organ." Is that a surprising statement? It's no wonder we pay so much attention to skin. In the following poem, "Two Countries," Nye uses skin as the main character. As you read, remember to write your questions and comments in the **Response Notes** column.

Two Countries by Naomi Shihab Nye

Skin remembers how long the years grow
when skin is not touched, a gray tunnel
of singleness, feather lost from the tail
of a bird, swirling onto a step,
swept away by someone who never saw
it was a feather. Skin ate, walked,
slept by itself, knew how to raise a
see-you-later hand. But skin felt
it was never seen, never known as
a land on the map, nose like a city,
hip like a city, gleaming dome of the mosque
and the hundred corridors of cinnamon and rope.

Skin had hope, that's what skin does.
Heals over the scarred place, makes a road.
Love means you breathe in two countries.
And skin remembers—silk, spiny grass,
deep in the pocket that is skin's secret own.
Even now, when skin is not alone,
it remembers being alone and thanks something
larger that there are travelers, that people go places
larger than themselves.

Response Notes

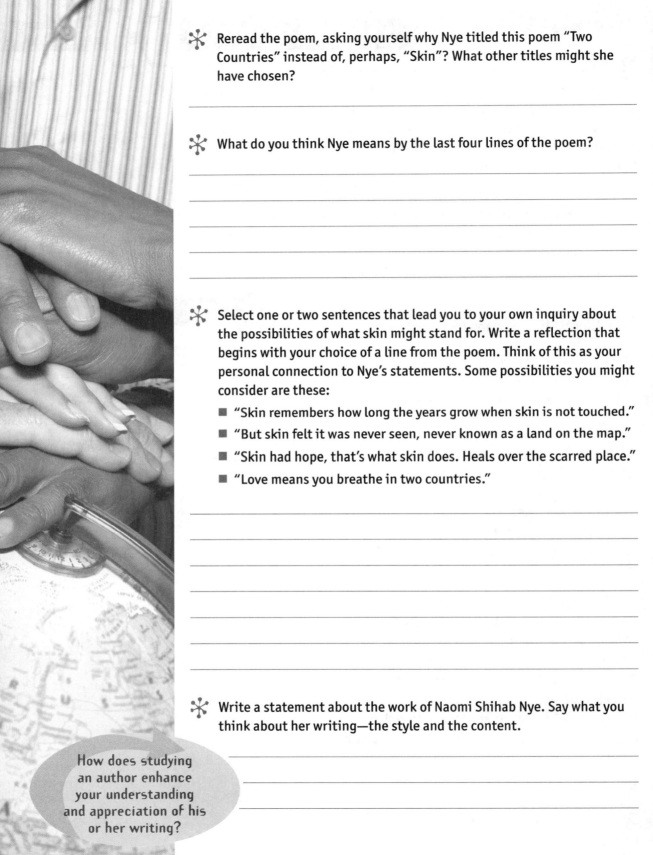

✳ Reread the poem, asking yourself why Nye titled this poem "Two Countries" instead of, perhaps, "Skin"? What other titles might she have chosen?

_____

✳ What do you think Nye means by the last four lines of the poem?

_____

_____

_____

_____

✳ Select one or two sentences that lead you to your own inquiry about the possibilities of what skin might stand for. Write a reflection that begins with your choice of a line from the poem. Think of this as your personal connection to Nye's statements. Some possibilities you might consider are these:

■ "Skin remembers how long the years grow when skin is not touched."

■ "But skin felt it was never seen, never known as a land on the map."

■ "Skin had hope, that's what skin does. Heals over the scarred place."

■ "Love means you breathe in two countries."

_____

_____

_____

_____

_____

✳ Write a statement about the work of Naomi Shihab Nye. Say what you think about her writing—the style and the content.

_____

_____

_____

How does studying an author enhance your understanding and appreciation of his or her writing?

Investigating a Genre

The lights go down. The curtain opens on another world. For a time, everyone is transported into the lives of the characters on the stage. The work that has gone into this play is huge—casting, costuming, set design. The actors have had to become their characters and learn their lines. Guiding the process are the playwright, the script, and the director's vision.

In this unit, you will use the five essential strategies that you have practiced throughout this *Daybook*. They are tailored to help you investigate **drama** as a genre. Ask yourself how you can learn about drama using the strategies.

War of the Words is a one-act play by Robin F. Brancato, an author of novels for young adults and a former high school teacher. In the stage directions, she explains "*War of the Words* illustrates the conflict between two rival teenage gangs, The Notes and The Grunts. These adversaries have long struggled to defend their turf—that is, their respective sides of the urban schoolyard. The cause of the contention between them is not ethnic diversity or class rivalries, but irreconcilable differences in communication. The Notes are pretentious, effete sissies who speak in iambic pentameter—usually even in rhymed couplets; the Grunts, at the other extreme, speak in clichés, fragments of esoteric slang, and monosyllabic grunts." Turn the page to meet the cast of characters and to see how their conflicts "play" out.

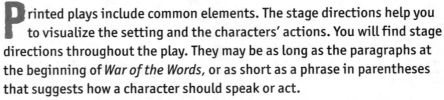

Printed plays include common elements. The stage directions help you to visualize the setting and the characters' actions. You will find stage directions throughout the play. They may be as long as the paragraphs at the beginning of *War of the Words*, or as short as a phrase in parentheses that suggests how a character should speak or act.

The character list or cast of characters may also suggest how the characters could look and act. Make notes on the character list about how you think each character will look, based just on his or her name.

CHARACTERS

THE NOTES:	THE GRUNTS:
Homer, the leader	Buzz, the leader
Dante	Spike
William	Punch
Guinevere	Bette
Desiree	Dot
Lucinda, not officially a Note; a new girl in town, admired by Homer	Moll

You read the first part of the stage directions on page 211. As you read the rest of the stage directions, draw in the **Response Notes** all the objects that you see and highlight in the text all the actions. Also, list actions that you think you would see when the play is being performed.

from **War of the Words** by Robin F. Brancato

The Notes males wear stereotypical outfits that suggest "poet" or "romantic." That is, one wears a velvet jacket, another a cape and beret, the third a shirt with a ruffle at the neck. On the back of each costume is each one's name and an emblem that says "Notes" along with musical notes ♩ ♫ , such as would be seen on jackets worn by a typical gang. Their hair is long, and their manners are exaggeratedly polite, even affected.

The Notes females are dressed in frilly clothes, such as *Gone With the Wind*-style hoopskirts, or long dresses of flimsy material, or very feminine peasant dresses. Guinevere and Desiree wear their names and the Notes emblem on their dresses. Their hair is carefully arranged. Lucinda is dressed like the female Notes but with no emblems on her clothing.

The Grunts males, all with crewcuts, are wearing as little clothing as possible because they want their muscles to show. They wear tight jeans or shorts, sleeveless shirts made of fishnet, or skintight T-shirts with slogans such as "The Grunts—Ugh" or "If You Want Me, Grunt."

The Grunts females are decked out in short skirts and low-cut tops in Day-Glo colors. Their hair is teased into bushy halos. They may be wearing Grunt emblems on their outfits also.

War of the Words is intended to include actor and audience participation. The actors are invited, before going into production, to change the script— that is, to add or fuse characters, depending on the number of participants available. Lines consistent with the speech of the two gangs and with the spirit of the play may be added to the existing script, and the poems that make up the competition at the end of the play are to be written, in advance, by the actors.

Music may also be added in appropriate places. For instance, at the outset of the play one of the Notes may be serenading his lady love on a flute or a recorder. The Grunts, especially the females when they are bopping, may also improvise music or rhythm by beating on garbage can lids or other "found" musical instruments. Music may be used throughout as a background and as a part of the competition at the end of the play.

SETTING

A school yard. The stage is divided in half by a length of fence that suggests an insurmountable barrier between the turf of the two gangs, THE NOTES *and* THE GRUNTS. *A painted backdrop shows the exterior of an urban school, complete with basketball hoops, graffiti, and an urban skyline in the distance. Stage right,* THE NOTES' *turf, features a flower-bedecked arbor and three park benches, or fancy garden chairs, or swings. Potted plants, either real or artificial, enhance the* NOTES' *territory. Graffiti on their side include hearts-and-flowers motifs and such sayings as "'Poetry is the spontaneous overflow of powerful feelings'—Wordsworth."*

THE GRUNTS' *turf is makeshift-urban-playground, strewn with such items as old tires, cement pipe, and garbage containers. Graffiti include crude sketches of knives dripping blood and such sayings as "Buzz Don't Take Nothin' from Nobody" and "Yur Mudder's Got a Mustache."*

When the curtain opens, the three NOTES *couples are frozen in a romantic tableau.* DANTE *is serenading* GUINEVERE *with a flute.* WILLIAM, *kneeling, offers an armful of flowers to* DESIREE, *and* HOMER, *in the center of* NOTES *turf, kisses* LUCINDA's *hand, stares at her soulfully, and whispers intimate secrets. Meanwhile the three* GRUNTS *males are sparring with each other, competing for space at the peephole in the fence that divides the territories, while* THE GRUNTS *females slouch near them, noisily cracking gum and bopping to the rhythm of a real or imaginary beat.*

SPIKE: Outta my way, punk!

PUNCH: Punch. *Punch* is m'name.

SPIKE: I know your punkin' name as well as I know my own. (*Tries to remember his own.*) Umm, umm . . . Spike! That's it, Spike! (*Shoves* PUNCH *with an elbow.*) Ain't we been Grunts together since we was grade school dropouts? Move oveh!

BUZZ (*bending his buddies' arms behind their backs*): Hey, Spike, Punch, let *me* look.

SPIKE and PUNCH (*intimidated*): Yeah, Buzz, yeah.

BUZZ: *Who's* the boss?

SPIKE and PUNCH: *You* are, Buzz. *You're* the boss.

BUZZ: Don't you forget it. Now, gimme some space. (*Stares through the peephole.*) What the punk are they doing today? Same punkin' sissy stuff like always, talking in poetry?

SPIKE: Yeah, worse than ever! They're gettin' out of hand.

PUNCH: They're pollutin' the air with that poetry, man.

BETTE: And hurting our eyeballs with those gaggy clothes they're wearing!

DOT: Somebody comes by here is gonna think *we're* part of them. Oooo! Noooo!

MOLL (*listening, hand cupped to ear*): They call that music? I could make better sounds blowin' into a bottle!

PUNCH: Let's rough up The Notes. Let's rip up their flowers and make holes in that flute.

BETTE: It's already got holes in it.

PUNCH: So *that's* why it sounds so bad.

SPIKE: Let's pound 'em in their voice boxes!

BUZZ: Yeah, they been asking for trouble. They been starting up like this every day.

SPIKE: Makin' low remarks about us. Actin' like they're better than us. Let's—

BUZZ (*shoving SPIKE away from the peephole again*): Shut up and let me hear what they're saying about us.

SPIKE *and* PUNCH *press their ears to the wall, and* BUZZ *returns to the peephole. The three of them react exaggeratedly to everything they hear with grimaces and gagging sounds.* THE GRUNTS *girls, meanwhile, pay attention off and on, but during the "off" times, they pull out supplies and begin primping and fixing each other's hair. Meanwhile, in* NOTES *territory . . .*

✳ Discuss with a partner the notes you made as you read. Add any images that help you better visualize the text. If you and your partner have differences, try to explain why you think that is.

_____

_____

_____

_____

_____

_____

In what ways do stage directions help you to visualize the action?

One way that we interpret stories is by **making connections.** This play, for example, might remind you of other plays or stories that you have read. It might remind you of films or television shows that you have seen. Many stories are based on conflicts between rivals. With a partner, brainstorm a list of such stories and write their titles in the box below.

Another way to interpret action and character in a play is to look at relationships. What connections exist and develop between characters? As you read the next part of *War of the Words*, make notes in the **Response Notes** column when you find out how the characters are connected to each other.

Response Notes

from **War of the Words** by Robin F. Brancato *(continued)*

HOMER: Lucinda is your name? When did you come?
　　　　And tell me all about the place you're from!

LUCINDA *(self-consciously)*: I've . . . I've been here, Homer, for so little time.
　　　　Does everyone who lives here talk in rhyme?

DANTE: Not everyone, Lucinda—the elite!
　　　　The brains like us, the ones you want to meet.
　　　　Meet Desiree, and William, over here.
　　　　I'm Dante and my love is Guinevere.

WILLIAM: Just don't go over *there*. You'll see the Grunts!
　　　　I'll guarantee you, every one's a dunce.

LUCINDA: I don't quite understand this. Why the wall?

GUINEVERE: To keep ourselves as pure as possible.

LUCINDA: What do they do to you? How do they speak?

DESIREE: Like hoodlums. Every one of them's a freak!

LUCINDA: But aren't they part of this—I mean the school?

HOMER: They're dropouts, mostly, trying to be cool.
　　　　They come here, after school, to taunt and mock,
　　　　And try to run us off the yard and block.

DANTE: It's shameful how they curse, and mangle words,
　　　　And call us fairies, sissies, wimps, and nerds!

DESIREE: The things they say! Especially Buzz, the cad!
   They've made the neighborhood go down.
   It's sad!

LUCINDA: And you don't bother them—you're innocent?

HOMER: They say we do, because their minds are bent.
   They say our voices interrupt their grunts,
   And that our music's terrible. And once
   They hurled a stink bomb at us, if you please,
   Because they said our flowers made them sneeze!

LUCINDA: I know I'm new here, but I can't quite see
   Why everyone must talk in poetry. . . .

There is a gradual change, beginning here, in BUZZ'S *reactions. He watches*
LUCINDA *more attentively through the peephole and begins to listen*
to her with real interest. SPIKE *and* PUNCH *continue to overreact to* THE
NOTES, *and* BETTE, DOT, *and* MOLL *continue to distract themselves with*
hair spray, curling irons, and sharp-bristled brushes.

HOMER: Because that's what we do! Because we're Notes!
   No ugly sound will e'er escape our throats!

DANTE: We can't stand hearing language that is crude,
   Like "Say, man," "Aw, your mudder!" or "Hey, dude!"

WILLIAM: Please, Dante, spare us hearing those harsh sounds!
   We hear enough from there, beyond the bounds!
   The fact is, poetry remains the test;
   Whoever speaks it obviously is best.

and PUNCH *become more agitated as they hear themselves talked about.*

SPIKE: You hear dat? We gonna just stand here and take abuse from those gags?

PUNCH *(enraged)*: Best! They think they're the best!

BUZZ, *still focused on* LUCINDA, *tries to quiet his buddies with a wave of his hand.*
Meanwhile, in NOTES *territory, the three couples continue whispering in poetry.*

MOLL: Crude! They called us crude!

BETTE: They say we make ugly sounds! They got a lotta nerve!

DOT: Harsh! They better watch who they're calling harsh!

Now the NOTES *can be heard speaking aloud again.* BUZZ *is completely*
fascinated with LUCINDA *now, so his former hostility has fizzled out.*

LUCINDA: Well, language is important, I agree,
   But not the only thing, it seems to me. . . .

GUINEVERE *(disagreeing)*: A crime, when people don't know how to speak—
   Their diction careless and their grammar weak.

DESIREE: And slang's another thing that I deplore;
    I'd much prefer a lovely metaphor.

HOMER: Lucinda's new here; she will come to see
    That perfect speech is a necessity.

From the other side of the fence come rude snorts and hoots from SPIKE *and* PUNCH. BUZZ *is still entranced by* LUCINDA. *From here on there is open verbal combat. Each remark is answered by the other side. All the males except* BUZZ *seem about to scale the fence and get at the enemy. The females, except* LUCINDA, *egg the males on.*

DANTE *(throwing up his hands in dismay)*: Those piglike noises from the
    other side
    Are sounds I can't in any way abide.

SPIKE: Poetry—Peeeuuuu!

WILLIAM *(dropping his flowers in shock)*: We can't stand by and hear
    ourselves maligned
    By boors and ruffians of this vicious kind!

MOLL (to SPIKE, PUNCH, and BUZZ): Hey, guys, aren'tcha gonna fight?
  Where's yuh pride? Where's yuh guts? Are ya Grunts or aren'tcha?

HOMER (to LUCINDA): You see? They're always first to sling the mud.
      And that's not all—they're really out for blood.

SPIKE: Blood! Dj'hear that? They just said they want our blood! Come on! We
  gotta waste 'em, man! *(He tugs at BUZZ's shirt, but BUZZ waves him away.)*

PUNCH: Whatsamatta, Buzzie baby? Sompin' botherin' ya? Ya sick?

By now, BUZZ *is sick—lovesick at the mere sight of* LUCINDA. *Ignoring his fellow* GRUNTS, *he continues to worship her through the peephole.*

GUINEVERE: They say we're sick. I can't believe their gall.
    Before we know it, they will scale the wall!

WILLIAM *(drawing everyone—except* LUCINDA, *who holds back—into a huddle)*:
    The best defense is offense. Let's attack.
    Let's plan a way to get them from the back.

SPIKE *(drawing everyone—except* BUZZ, *who holds back—into a huddle)*:
  Youse guys! Ferget Buzzie! He must be sick. Meanwhile they're gonna
  sneak up on us from da rear! Let's beat 'em to it. Come on! *(He leads all the*
  GRUNTS *except* BUZZ *offstage left.)*

HOMER *(rallying* THE NOTES, *except* LUCINDA, *and leading them offstage right)*:
    No time to waste. They're charging from the rear!
    A confrontation's imminent, I fear!

As soon as everyone else has gone, BUZZ *scales the wall and stands shyly but admiringly before* LUCINDA, *who smiles at him.*

BUZZ: Hi.

LUCINDA: Hi. Who are you? I feel we've met before.

BUZZ: Yeah? *(Grins and comes closer.)* Buzz's m'name. Lucinda?

LUCINDA *(nodding)*: Are you a Grunt? You're not so bad, I'd say.
So strange, that all The Notes have run away.

BUZZ: They're about to beat on us. They think they're better than us.

LUCINDA: They only want to talk in poetry;
That's not so big a crime, if you ask me.

BUZZ *(backing off)*: You're one of them.

LUCINDA: No, no, or if I am, it's accident.
I like you, too. Now tell me where they went.

BUZZ *(suspicious, but can't help being drawn to her)*:
Like Grunts and Notes, we hate each others' guts. . . .

LUCINDA: You think they treat you like a bunch of mutts.

BUZZ: Yeah! *(Pauses.)* Wait a minute. You *are* one of them! You talk like they do!

LUCINDA: Don't mean to. Just that I have been with them. . . .

BUZZ *(approaching her slowly and taking both her hands in his)*: It don't matter. Talk however you want. June, moon, spoon, the whole bit, don't matter to me. Just so I—Just so we can see each other. Alone. I ain't never felt like this before.

LUCINDA: I want to see you, too—we'll find a way. It won't be easy—*(Catching herself, she breaks out of iambic pentameter.)* They consider me one of them—a Note. Homer has already asked me to the prom.

BUZZ: No! Tell him no! You can't go with one of them show-offy gags! You aren't like them!

LUCINDA: I know. I know I'm not. I'm just myself.

BUZZ *(taking her in his arms)*: Let's get outta here. Let's get away from alla this. ✥

✳ The conflicts in a play usually arise from the characters and their relationships. Knowing what you know, predict what will happen next.

> What plot patterns do you find in texts that are based on conflicts between rivals?

68 EXPLORING CHARACTERS' PERSPECTIVES

If you have read other plays, you know that playwrights use **speech tags** to show who is speaking. In a play, dialogue can serve at least three purposes. The characters' lines establish who they are, advance the plot, and help develop the themes. Fill in the chart below with what you know about each character's point of view of or perspective on the conflict between the gangs. Use dialogue from the play to support what you know.

	Perspective on the conflict	Dialogue
Lucinda	Doesn't like the wall	"But aren't they part of this— I mean the school?"
Homer		
Buzz		

The different **perspectives** keep the **conflict** going and, in the end, contribute to resolving it. As you read the next part of the play, learn more about each character's perspective and about the central conflict. Label the dialogue with a **C** if it reveals something about the character, a **P** if it advances the plot, and a **T** if it relates to a theme.

from War of the Words by Robin F. Brancato *(continued)*

BUZZ *(taking her in his arms)*: Let's get outta here. Let's get away from alla this.

Muttering voices behind the backdrop become louder and escalate into a shouting match between the two gangs. Scuffling sounds are heard, and BUZZ and LUCINDA listen in horror.

PUNCH: Yur mudder talks broken English! *(Scuffle, pow, pow!)*

DANTE: No insult could be worse than that to me!
You'll pay for that, you Grunt, just wait and see! *(Wham! Crack!)*

DOT: Get 'im, Punch! Tear that gaggy lace off his shirt! *(Pow! Bang! Slam!)*

GUINEVERE: Help, help! What's that they have inside that bag?
Oh, no! They're going to tie us with a gag!

SPIKE: Yeah, gags to finally keep these gaggy kids quiet! Every Grunt's going to catch a Note and tie their mouth shut for good!

A chase begins backstage and ends onstage, GUINEVERE and DESIREE are already gagged when they appear, the captives of THE GRUNTS, but HOMER, DANTE, and WILLIAM are putting up a good fight. BUZZ pulls LUCINDA out of danger, and it is at this point that HOMER, struggling to keep the gag off his mouth, sees BUZZ and LUCINDA together for the first time. He sputters with anger, and when he speaks, there is a temporary halt to the rumble.

HOMER: Unhand her, villain! Woman, come to me.

BUZZ *(holding on to LUCINDA firmly)*: I'm not handing her over to no gaggy poet.

HOMER: Lucinda, tell him you belong with us.

LUCINDA *(confused)*: I'm not so sure I do—why all the fuss?

HOMER *(striding threateningly toward BUZZ)*: Unhand her, or your life is on the line;
I'm quite prepared to risk the loss of mine.

Each gang now rallies behind its leader—i.e., behind HOMER and BUZZ, who face each other, ready for combat, WILLIAM and DANTE untie the gags of GUINEVERE and DESIREE, murmurs of encouragement are heard on both sides, and then, simultaneously, HOMER and BUZZ throw punches at each other.

LUCINDA *(intervening between them—to HOMER)*: This can't be happening.
No way it can
Whoever wants my love must be a *man.*
(To BUZZ): Look, violence is ridiculous. If you can't settle this peacefully, I have an idea. You two have a fair fight—a wrestling match, for instance. Whoever wins, I'll go out with—for the time being, anyway.

DANTE: A wrestling match! How vulgar, like TV!

WILLIAM: A duel with swords is what the fight should be.

PUNCH: Nah. A street fight, and right now, fighting only with what we got on us.

PUNCH whispers to SPIKE and BUZZ, who pull out of their pockets weapons such as pocket knives and beer can openers. THE GRUNTS girls prepare to use their hair spray cans, curling irons, and brushes as weapons. All THE GRUNTS stand armed and ready.

This is going to cause a problem.

DESIREE: That isn't fair—we never carry arms.
　　　Our only armor's our poetic charms.

LUCINDA (*to* THE NOTES, *desperately, as a way of stalling the fighting*):
　　　So flip a coin before you start to fight.
　　　Whoever wins will choose the weapon, right?

(*To* THE GRUNTS): Hey, come on, you guys, Please let's settle this without
　anybody getting hurt!

BUZZ: Fair enough, what you just said. (*Throws her a quarter.*) Flip the coin.
　Heads, they pick the weapon; tails, we pick. Whatever weapon gets picked,
　it's me against him (*pointing to* HOMER). Winner walks off with Cindy, and
　nobody, no Note and no Grunt, stands in the way.

HOMER: Her name's Lucinda, Grunt—let's get it right!
　　　Why, that alone is cause enough to fight!

LUCINDA (*coming between them*): Now, Homer, where is it you think you're goin'?
　　　　　　　Agree that you will let me flip the coin.

*Each gang gets into a huddle to discuss this suggestion. Coming out of their
huddles, HOMER and BUZZ both nod their agreement to the terms. LUCINDA
stands apart, nervously fingering the quarter and eyeing the two gang leaders.*

LUCINDA: I like you both. This tears me up, I swear!
　　　I hate to flip the coin. . . .

HOMER: Come on, fair's fair.

THE GRUNTS: Come on, flip! Hurry up! Whatcha waitin' for?

LUCINDA (*flips the coin*): Heads.

THE NOTES, *cheering because they have won the toss, regroup into their
huddle, while* THE GRUNTS *slouch awkwardly, waiting to hear about the choice
of weapons. After a second* HOMER *comes triumphantly out of the huddle.*

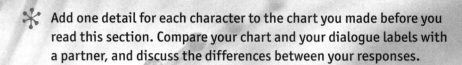

✳ Add one detail for each character to the chart you made before you
read this section. Compare your chart and your dialogue labels with
a partner, and discuss the differences between your responses.

How do the
perspectives of the
characters suggest what
might happen next?

Any kind of text can include **dialogue**, but it is central to a play. As you have seen so far, the two gangs in this play are defined by how they use language. The Grunts prefer slang, and the Notes prefer poetry. They express their contempt for each other with fists and insults. Robin Brancato invited you to add or delete lines and to change the personalities of the characters. You might also want to change the slang to words that are more contemporary or more familiar in your geographic area. Some slang expressions are more popular at different times or in different places and could even characterize the speaker as someone from a particular group.

✳ Discuss with a partner the people you envision using the following words: *way cool, dis, awesome*. Think about a particular group that you know well and list five slang words they use among themselves. Be sure these words are appropriate for a school group to read or hear. Write the words and their meanings in the space below.

_____

_____

_____

_____

_____

The Notes do not talk in slang. They use *rhymed couplets of iambic pentameter*. The couplet may be spoken by one person or shared by two.

> DANTE: A wrestling match! How vulgar, like TV!
> WILLIAM: A duel with swords is what the fight should be.

✳ Do you hear how *TV* and *be* rhyme? This is called a **rhymed couplet** because the two lines rhyme at the end, and no other lines are between them. **Iambic pentameter** tells how many stressed syllables there will be in a line; *pentameter* means "five." An iamb is a pair of syllables in which the first is unstressed and the second is stressed. Say the lines aloud, stressing the syllable that has a / over it, and not stressing the one with a ˘ over it.

˘	/	˘	/	˘	/	˘	/	˘	/
A	wrest	ling	match	How	vul	gar	like	T	V

✳ As you read the next section of *War of the Words*, mark the rhymed couplets. Also, notice how Lucinda talks. Is her language more like the Notes or the Grunts, or is it her own? How does her language fit her character? Make notes as you read.

Response Notes

HOMER: We've found the perfect way to kill you birds.
　　　The weapon we are choosing will be . . . words!

GRUNTS: Huh? Wha—? Come off it! Punkin' sissies—*words?*

LUCINDA: Words?

WILLIAM *(smugly)*: Yes, words as weapons; words will win the day!
　　　The pen is stronger than the sword, they say.

GUINEVERE: We'll stage a battle, all in poetry,
　　　Whoe'er performs the best claims victory.

SPIKE: Hey, wha—?

PUNCH: No punkin' fair!

BETTE, DOT, MOLL: They'll kill us fer sure!

HOMER *(gloating)*: Each group will write a verse, and when we're done,
　　　Then Buzz and I'll recite them, one on one.

BUZZ: Ya mean I gotta beat him at recitin' a punkin' *poem?*

BETTE: We gotta *write* it first—that's worse!

SPIKE: Forget it. *(Pulls out his knife.)* We changed our minds. Street fight—
　　that's what we want.

BUZZ *(smiling shyly at* LUCINDA*)*: Nah. We agreed. We got our pride. We'll do
　　it—we're Grunts!

PUNCH: How long is a poem?

DESIREE: A poem has no set length and no set form;
　　　For sonnets, fourteen lines would be the norm.

MOLL: *Sonnets?* What's she talkin', Greek?

GUINEVERE: Although a poem doesn't have to rhyme,
　　　Rhymed couplets are, I think, the most sublime.

DOT: Rhymed *what?*

BUZZ: Hey. Okay, so we—we'll write a poem. And I'll say it. How do we know
　　who wins? It can't be up to you gags.

HOMER: We, of course, will judge—don't mean to boast,
　　　But certainly it's clear—we know the most.

SPIKE: No punkin' fair!

LUCINDA: He's right. It isn't fair. You can't compete and judge at the same
　　time. There's only one fair way to do it. After both sides have written their
　　verses, we'll call in an outside audience and let them make a decision by
　　the length and loudness of their applause.

WILLIAM: The audience may not be in the know;
      They might like comic books instead of Poe.

BETTE: Tough jelly beans! That's the chance you take! We'll get our tightest friends to be the audience.

DESIREE: *Our* friends will gladly come to help us out.
      True poetry will win without a doubt.

BUZZ: How long we got to come up with this thing?

LUCINDA (*thinking fast*): We'll get permission to call for an audience over the football field loudspeaker, and while kids are gathering here, you'll write your words. It might be hard, though, to have a contest here, with this wall in the way. Maybe we should take it down.

PUNCH: Take the wall down? So what'll we look through, when we wanta see what they're doin'? (SPIKE *punches him for his stupidity.*)

DANTE: The wall protects us from gross sights and sound.
      For just this contest, though, let's take it down.

BUZZ *and* HOMER *assess the feelings of their groups and then nod reluctantly at* LUCINDA.

LUCINDA: I'd love to see the wall come down right now. Let's do it. Which of you can show us how?

Everybody from both gangs kicks and pushes until the wall topples. At first they are all gleeful, but then, remembering they're supposed to be enemies, they regroup into opposing gangs.

LUCINDA (*aside*): Regardless of how things turn out, I, for one, hope never to see that wall again. (*To both gangs*) I'm going to get permission to make the announcement over the loudspeaker. While I'm gone, get busy. Ready, get set, write!

As both gangs dive into huddles, on their own turf, and furiously begin to organize and create, LUCINDA *exits and the stage goes dark. Within a few seconds the announcement blares.* ❖

In her last speech, Lucinda speaks to the audience as if the actors cannot hear her. This is called an **aside**, and it is a dramatic technique used to reveal a character's thoughts.

✳ Choose one of the characters. Write an aside that he or she could say at this point in the play.

_____

_____

How does dialogue help to define character?

By entering the world of the Notes and the Grunts in this play, you have probably become familiar with their language. In this lesson, you will write the poem that Buzz or Homer will use to compete for Lucinda's attention.

Remember that both boys like Lucinda, but she will choose only one of them. Write a poem that will persuade her to choose you. As prewriting, review the play to answer the following questions about the role of the character you are writing for—Buzz or Homer.

1 What do I like so much about Lucinda? _____

_____

_____

_____

2 What does Lucinda seem to like? _____

_____

_____

_____

3 What do I want to write about? _____

_____

_____

4 What are the best words I've used in the play so far? _____

_____

_____

5 What form do I want to use for my poem—rhymed couplets, some other form, or no particular form? What will be effective about that form?

_____

_____

_____

_____

✳ Write a draft of your poem here.

_____

_____

_____

_____

_____

_____

_____

_____

_____

_____

_____

_____

_____

_____

_____

_____

_____

_____

_____

✳ Read the end of the play aloud in a group that has an equal number of poems from Buzz and Homer. When it's time for the competition, read your poems. Let the whole group help Lucinda choose the winner.

from **War of the Words** by Robin F. Brancato *(continued)*

AMPLIFIED VOICE: Attention! We'll announce this only once—
      A showdown, now, between The Notes and Grunts.
      For once and all, these enemies will clash;
      Come running, now, to hear who wins this bash.

    Hey, all you students, and jocks, and streetwise guys and gals. Book over here, ya hear? The verbal rumble is on. We need ya to listen up good and put these gangs to the test to figure out which of 'em is best.
A few extras come from behind the curtain and sit down among the actual audience to create the illusion of an audience gathering. The stage lights up

Response
Notes

again, and LUCINDA *reappears at stage center. She shouts "Stop writing!" and both gangs follow her orders. The two leaders prepare to face off on the spot where the wall was, and their respective gangs are seated behind them, ready to cheer them on. LUCINDA supervises the flipping of a coin to determine who will go first.*

LUCINDA: Heads it is—The Notes will go first.

Okay, the contest's ready to begin.

Good luck to both, and may the best gang win.

At this point the two original actor-written verses are delivered, the first by HOMER *and the second by* BUZZ. *After both poems have been recited,* LUCINDA *calls for applause from the actual audience, and she determines who the winner is. She then holds up his arm, as in a championship boxing match, and she walks off the stage with him, followed by both gangs, who accept the results peacefully. The curtain falls on a quiet school yard with no dividing wall.*

CURTAIN ✧

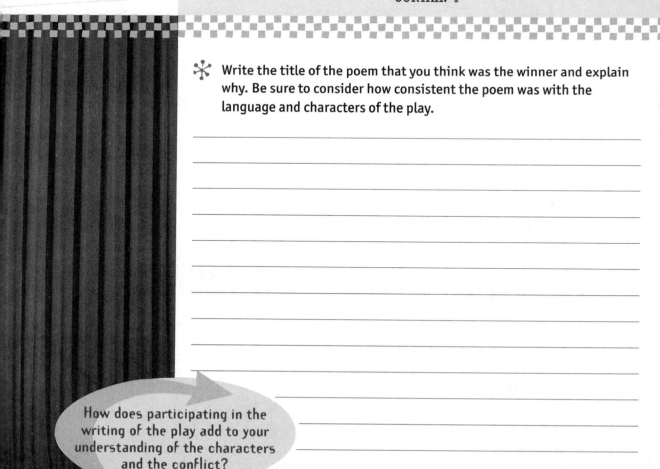

✳ Write the title of the poem that you think was the winner and explain why. Be sure to consider how consistent the poem was with the language and characters of the play.

_____

_____

_____

_____

_____

_____

_____

_____

_____

How does participating in the writing of the play add to your understanding of the characters and the conflict?

_____

Investigating the Reflective Essay

You have encountered the word *reflection* or *reflective* a number of times in this *Daybook*. You have written reflective comments in your **Response Notes**; you have written short, reflective paragraphs about the meaning of a piece of literature. You have also read some reflective poems, essays, and stories that asked you to step back and think about what they meant.

In this unit, you will read two examples of the **reflective essay**. Using the inquiry method, you will gather information about what makes a reflective essay different from a conventional autobiographical essay, a descriptive essay, or a personal narrative.

Both of the essays were written about an unexpected meeting with an animal that people rarely see. As you read, you will learn how naturalists behave when they encounter an unusual situation. You will also get ideas about how to write reflective essays of your own.

WHAT THE WRITER SEES

A reflective essay often takes the form of a memoir, which is a remembrance of an event or a period in a narrator's life. The **reflective essay**, however, is more than a retelling of the event. In a reflective essay, the writer thinks about the event and asks the reader to think about it, too.

Read the excerpt from Edward Abbey's essay "Freedom and Wilderness," using the **Response Notes** column to record your questions and make comments. Some of the ways to respond include the following:

- Writing notes about details that stand out
- Asking questions about the use of certain words or phrases
- Writing notes about anything similar to your own experiences
- Noting comments about parts of the essay that you think are especially interesting
- Writing observations about the act of reflecting

Response Notes

from Freedom and Wilderness by Edward Abbey

A couple of years ago I had a job. I worked for an outfit called Defenders of Fur Bearers (now known as Defenders of Wildlife). I was caretaker and head janitor of a 70,000-acre wildlife refuge in the vicinity of Aravaipa Canyon in southern Arizona. The Whittell Wildlife Preserve, as we called it, was a refuge for mountain lion, javelina, a few black bear, maybe a wolf or two, a herd of whitetail deer, and me, to name the principal fur bearers.

I was walking along Aravaipa Creek one afternoon when I noticed fresh mountain lion tracks leading ahead of me. Big tracks, the biggest lion tracks I've seen anywhere. Now I've lived most of my life in the Southwest, but I am sorry to admit that I had never seen a mountain lion in the wild. Naturally I was eager to get a glimpse of this one.

It was getting late in the day, the sun already down beyond the canyon wall, so I hurried along, hoping I might catch up to the lion and get one good look at him before I had to turn back and head home. But no matter how fast I walked and then jogged along, I couldn't seem to get any closer; those big tracks kept leading ahead of me, looking not five minutes old, but always disappearing around the next turn in the canyon.

I'd be excited but scared!

Twilight settled in, visibility getting poor. I realized I'd have to call it quits. I stopped for a while, staring upstream into the gloom of the canyon. I could see the buzzards settling down for the evening in their favorite dead cottonwood. I heard the poor-wills and the spotted toads beginning to sing, but of that mountain lion I could neither hear nor see any living trace.

I turned around and started home. I'd walked maybe a mile when I thought I heard something odd behind me. I stopped and looked back—nothing; nothing but the canyon, the running water, the trees, the rocks, the willow thickets. I went on and soon I heard that noise again—the sound of footsteps.

I stopped. The noise stopped. Feeling a bit uncomfortable now—it was getting dark—with all the ancient superstitions of the night starting to crawl from the crannies of my soul, I looked back again. And this time I saw him. About fifty yards behind me, poised on a sand bar, one front paw still lifted and waiting, stood this big cat, looking straight at me. I could see the gleam of the twilight in his eyes. I was startled as always by how small a cougar's head seems but how long and lean and powerful the body really is. To me, at that moment, he looked like the biggest cat in the world. He looked dangerous. Now I know very well that mountain lions are supposed almost never to attack human beings. I knew there was nothing to fear—but I couldn't help thinking maybe this lion is different from the others. Maybe he knows we're in a wildlife preserve, where lions can get away with anything. I was not unarmed; I had my Swiss army knife in my pocket with the built-in can opener, the corkscrew, the two-inch folding blade, the screwdriver. Rationally there was nothing to fear; all the same I felt fear.

And something else, too: I felt what I always feel when I meet a large animal face to face in the wild: I felt a kind of affection and the crazy desire to communicate, to make some kind of emotional, even physical contact with the animal. After we'd stared at each other for maybe five seconds—it seemed at the time like five minutes—I held out one hand and took a step toward the big cat and said something ridiculous like, "Here kitty, kitty." The cat paused there on three legs, one paw up as if he wanted to shake hands. But he didn't respond to my advance.

I took a second step toward the lion. Again the lion remained still, not moving a muscle, not blinking an eye. And I stopped and thought again and this time I understood that however the big cat might secretly feel, I myself was not yet quite ready to shake hands with a mountain lion. Maybe someday. But not yet. I retreated.

I turned and walked homeward again, pausing every few steps to look back over my shoulder. The cat had lowered his front paw but did not follow me. The last I saw of him, from the next bend of the canyon, he was still in the same place, watching me go. I hurried on through the evening, stopping now and then to look and listen, but if that cat followed me any further I could detect no sight or sound of it.

I haven't seen a mountain lion since that evening, but the experience remains shining in my memory. I want my children to have the opportunity for that kind of experience. I want my friends to have it. I want even our enemies to have it—they need it most. And someday, possibly, one of our children's children will discover how to get close enough to that mountain lion to shake paws with it, to embrace and caress it, maybe even teach it something, and to learn what the lion has to teach us. ❖

INVESTIGATING THE ELEMENTS OF A REFLECTIVE ESSAY

To investigate different aspects of the reflective essay, first, you will look at observational details, what Abbey observed. Later, you will look at structure.

✳ What is the strongest picture or image that you had when you finished reading this essay? Sketch it in the box below.

[sketch box]

TITLE

✳ Title your picture and write a few sentences about why you chose to draw this image.

_____

_____

_____

✳ Share your picture with a partner or a group and compare the images that your partner or group members selected.

> How does drawing an image from an essay affect the way you notice the observational details?

You have noticed the details in the essay. Now look at how the essay is structured. There are several steps, or events, in the story line.

1. List the key events in Abbey's story line in the left column of the chart below.

2. Look for words that tell you what the author is thinking about as the story unfolds. Put these ideas in the middle column.

3. In the right column, write your own reflections—your thoughts about what happened.

Events in the story line	Abbey's reflections	Your reflections
noticed mountain lion tracks	eager to see the mountain lion	I might not be as eager.

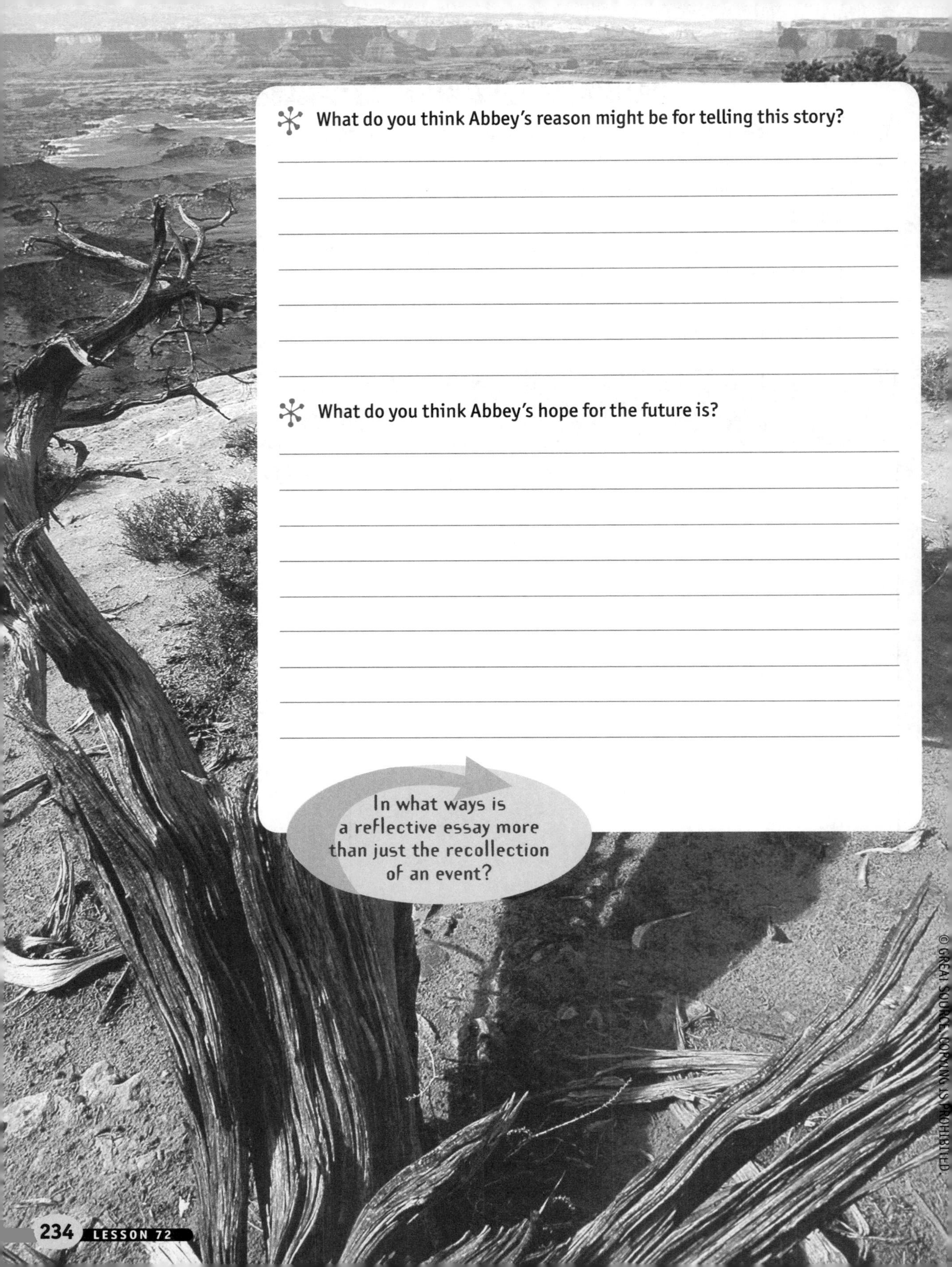

✳ **What do you think Abbey's reason might be for telling this story?**

_____

_____

_____

_____

_____

_____

✳ **What do you think Abbey's hope for the future is?**

_____

_____

_____

_____

_____

_____

_____

_____

_____

In what ways is
a reflective essay more
than just the recollection
of an event?

In reading "Living Like Weasels" by Annie Dillard, you'll see that this reflective essay is organized quite differently from Edward Abbey's. Read the first part now, making notations in the **Response Notes** about your observations.

Living Like Weasels by Annie Dillard

A weasel is wild. Who knows what he <u>thinks</u>? He sleeps in his underground den, his tail draped over his nose. Sometimes he lives in his den for two days without leaving. Outside, he stalks rabbits, mice, muskrats, and birds, killing more bodies than he can eat warm, and often dragging the carcasses home. Obedient to instinct, he bites his prey at the neck, either splitting the jugular vein at the throat or crunching the brain at the base of the skull, and he does not let go. One naturalist refused to kill a weasel who was socketed into his hand deeply as a rattlesnake. The man could in no way pry the tiny weasel off, and he had to walk half a mile to water, the weasel dangling from his palm, and soak him off like a stubborn label.

And once, says Ernest Thompson Seton—once, a man shot an eagle out of the sky. He examined the eagle and found the dry skull of a weasel fixed by the jaws to his throat. The supposition is that the eagle had pounced on the weasel and the weasel swiveled and bit as instinct taught him, tooth to neck, and nearly won. I would like to have seen that eagle from the air a few weeks or months before he was shot: was the whole weasel still attached to his feathered throat, a fur pendant? Or did the eagle eat what he could reach, gutting the living weasel with his talons before his breast, bending his beak, cleaning the beautiful airborne bones?

Response Notes

Do most people think that animals "think"?

✳ **What have you learned about weasels so far?**

_____

_____

_____

_____

_____

_____

_____

_____

Now continue with your reading.

I have been reading about weasels because I saw one last week. I startled a weasel who startled me, and we exchanged a long glance.

Twenty minutes from my house, through the woods by the quarry and across the highway, is Hollins Pond, a remarkable piece of shallowness, where I like to go at sunset and sit on a tree trunk. Hollins Pond is also called Murray's Pond; it covers two acres of bottomland near Tinker Creek with six inches of water and six thousand lily pads. In winter, brown-and-white steers stand in the middle of it, merely dampening their hooves; from the distant shore they look like miracle itself, complete with miracle's nonchalance. Now, in summer, the steers are gone. The water lilies have blossomed and spread to a green horizontal plane that is terra firma to plodding blackbirds, and tremulous ceiling to black leeches, crayfish, and carp.

This is, mind you, suburbia. It is a five-minute walk in three directions to rows of houses, though none is visible here. There's a 55-mph highway at one end of the pond, and a nesting pair of wood ducks at the other. Under every bush is a muskrat hole or a beer can. The far end is an alternating series of fields and woods, fields and woods, threaded everywhere with motorcycle tracks—in whose bare clay wild turtles lay eggs.

So, I had crossed the highway, stepped over two low barbed-wire fences, and traced the motorcycle path in all gratitude through the wild rose and poison ivy of the pond's shoreline up into high grassy fields. Then I cut down through the woods to the mossy fallen tree where I sit. This tree is excellent. It makes a dry, upholstered bench at the upper, marshy end of the pond, a plush jetty raised from the thorny shore between a shallow blue body of water and a deep blue body of sky.

What a peaceful scene

The sun had just set. I was relaxed on the tree trunk, ensconced in the lap of lichen, watching the lily pads at my feet tremble and part dreamily over the thrusting path of a carp. A yellow bird appeared to my right and flew behind me. It caught my eye; I swiveled around—and the next instant, inexplicably, I was looking down at a weasel, who was looking up at me.

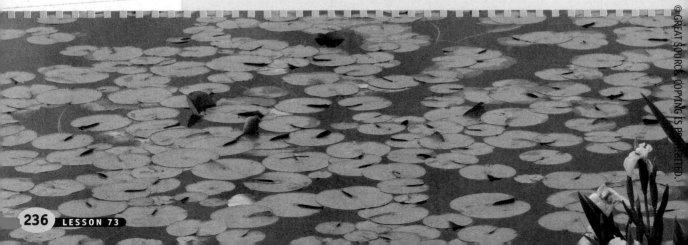

✳ Dillard describes in great detail the surroundings of her suburban home. From the details she gives you, see how closely you can map the area. Work alone or with a partner and share your results.

Read the next section to experience the actual encounter with the weasel.

Weasel! I'd never seen one wild before. He was ten inches long, thin as a curve, a muscled ribbon, brown as fruitwood, soft-furred, alert. His face was fierce, small and pointed as a lizard's; he would have made a good arrowhead. There was just a dot of chin, maybe two brown hairs' worth, and then the pure white fur began that spread down his underside. He had two black eyes I didn't see, any more than you see a window.

The weasel was stunned into stillness as he was emerging from beneath an enormous shaggy wild rose bush four feet away. I was stunned into stillness twisted backward on the tree trunk. Our eyes locked, and someone threw away the key.

Our look was as if two lovers, or deadly enemies, met unexpectedly on an overgrown path when each had been thinking of something else: a clearing blow to the gut. It was also a bright blow to the brain, or a sudden beating of brains, with all the charge and intimate grate of rubbed balloons. It emptied our lungs. It felled the forest, moved the fields, and drained the pond; the world dismantled and tumbled into that black hole of eyes. If you and I looked at each other that way, our skulls would split and drop to our shoulders. But we don't. We keep our skulls. So.

He disappeared. This was only last week, and already I don't remember what shattered the enchantment. I think I blinked, I think I retrieved my brain from the weasel's brain, and tried to memorize what I was seeing, and the weasel felt the yank of separation, the careening splash-down into real life and the urgent current of instinct. He vanished under the wild rose. I waited motionless, my mind suddenly full of data and my spirit with pleadings, but he didn't return. ✦

Dillard writes vivid images in this description of what happens when she confronts a weasel. Choose two sentences that you think are difficult to understand, outrageous in their meaning, or fascinating in their imagery. Write the sentences here, and then write your reflections about them.

Sentences from the essay	My reflections

Why do you think the author describes the surroundings so fully before she gets to the encounter with the weasel?

Read the last part of the essay. Continue to note your observations and connections.

from **Living Like Weasels** by Annie Dillard

Please do not tell me about "approach-avoidance conflicts." I tell you I've been in that weasel's brain for sixty seconds, and he was in mine. Brains are private places, muttering through unique and secret tapes—but the weasel and I both plugged into another tape simultaneously, for a sweet and shocking time. Can I help it if it was a blank?

What goes on in his brain the rest of the time? What does a weasel think about? He won't say. His journal is tracks in clay, a spray of feathers, mouse blood and bone: uncollected, unconnected, loose leaf, and blown.

I would like to learn, or remember, how to live. I come to Hollins Pond not so much to learn how to live as, frankly, to forget about it. That is, I don't think I can learn from a wild animal how to live in particular—shall I suck warm blood, hold my tail high, walk with my footprints precisely over the prints of my hands?—but I might learn something of mindlessness, something of the purity of living in the physical sense and the dignity of living without bias or motive. The weasel lives in necessity and we live in choice, hating necessity and dying at the last ignobly in its talons. I would like to live as I should, as the weasel lives as he should. And I suspect that for me the way is like the weasel's: open to time and death painlessly, noticing everything, remembering nothing, choosing the given with a fierce and pointed will.

I missed my chance. I should have gone for the throat. I should have lunged for that streak of white under the weasel's chin and held on, held on through mud and into the wild rose, held on for a dearer life. We could live under the wild rose wild as weasels, mute and uncomprehending. I could very calmly go wild. I could live two days in the den, curled, leaning on mouse fur, sniffing bird bones, blinking, licking, breathing musk, my hair tangled in the roots of grasses. Down is a good place to go, where the mind is single. Down is out, out of your ever-loving mind and back to your careless senses. I remember muteness as a prolonged and giddy fast, where every moment is a feast of utterance received. Time and events are merely poured, unremarked, and ingested directly, like blood pulsed into my gut through a jugular vein. Could two live that way? Could two live under the wild rose, and explore by the pond, so that the smooth mind of each is as everywhere present to the other, and as received and as unchallenged, as falling snow?

We could, you know. We can live any way we want. People take vows of poverty, chastity, and obedience—even of silence—by choice. The thing is to stalk your calling in a certain skilled and supple way, to locate the most tender and live spot and plug into that pulse. This is yielding, not fighting. A weasel doesn't "attack" anything; a weasel lives as he's meant to, yielding at every moment to the perfect freedom of single necessity.

I think it would be well, and proper, and obedient, and pure, to grasp your one necessity and not let it go, to dangle from it limp wherever it takes you. Then even death, where you're going no matter how you live, cannot you part. Seize it and let it seize you up aloft even, till your eyes burn out and drop; let your musky flesh fall off in shreds, and let your very bones unhinge and scatter, loosened over fields, over fields and woods, lightly, thoughtless, from any height at all, from as high as eagles. ⁂

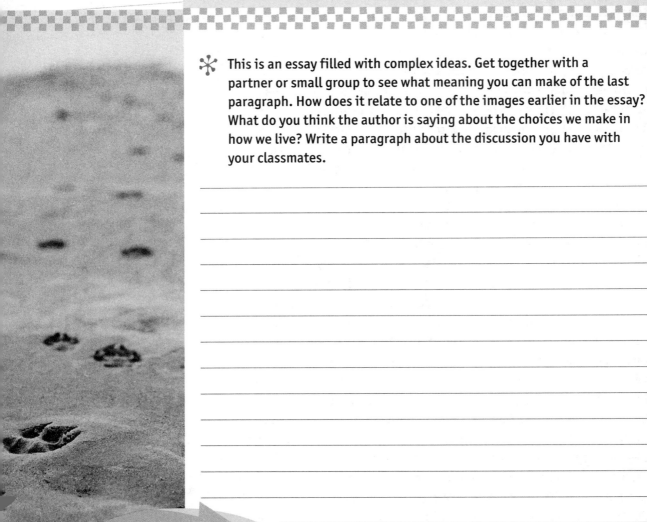

✳ This is an essay filled with complex ideas. Get together with a partner or small group to see what meaning you can make of the last paragraph. How does it relate to one of the images earlier in the essay? What do you think the author is saying about the choices we make in how we live? Write a paragraph about the discussion you have with your classmates.

_____

_____

_____

_____

_____

_____

_____

_____

_____

_____

_____

How does this essay go beyond a simple retelling of an afternoon walk through a natural park?

_____

_____

_____

You have read two reflective essays, each developed in a different way. Abbey's essay on "Freedom and Wilderness" reads much like a story. Abbey uses what we call **narrative strategies**, such as pacing, dialogue, and action, along with his reflections. Dillard, in "Living Like Weasels," is more reflective throughout the essay. She has a story line, a narrative about meeting up with the weasel, but it is sandwiched between sections of description and reflection.

There is no one way to write a reflective essay. However, these essays share certain characteristics:

- They present an occasion for reflection. This is usually some kind of event that the author presents as a narrative.

- They are rich in details, with specific descriptions of events, of surroundings, and of the subject—in these essays, the animals.

- They tell you what the writer is thinking, the larger ideas that stem from a particular incident.

Here are two quotations from the essays that include the reflections of the writers on their experiences.

- From the Abbey essay: "And someday, possibly, one of our children's children will discover how to get close enough to that mountain lion to shake paws with it, to embrace and caress it, maybe even teach it something, and to learn what the lion has to teach us."

- From the Dillard essay: "The weasel lives in necessity and we live in choice. . . . We can live any way we want."

Notice how these reflections are statements, not part of the story line. The author asks you to consider the story and then think about the statement. They aren't "conclusions" as an end to a story is. But they are conclusions in the sense that they wrap up the author's ideas about the meaning of the incident. Talk with a partner about these two quotations and how they serve as conclusions for their respective essays.

WRITE YOUR OWN ESSAY

Before you write your own reflective essay, you will need to select an occasion. To mimic the essays you have already read, you might choose an encounter with an animal. It could be an insect, a mammal, a bird, or another kind of animal. The occasion becomes the stimulus for the writer to explore and interpret an aspect of people in general or of people in relation to the natural world.

✳ Write notes about your encounter.

- Draw the setting if you think that will help clarify it in your mind.
- Include in your drawing clues to your thinking.
- What is the larger issue you might consider when you think about this incident?

✳ Use your own paper to write your essay. Write a rough draft. Then follow your teacher's guidelines for revising and finishing a final draft.

How has the study of these two essays helped you in writing your own reflective essay?

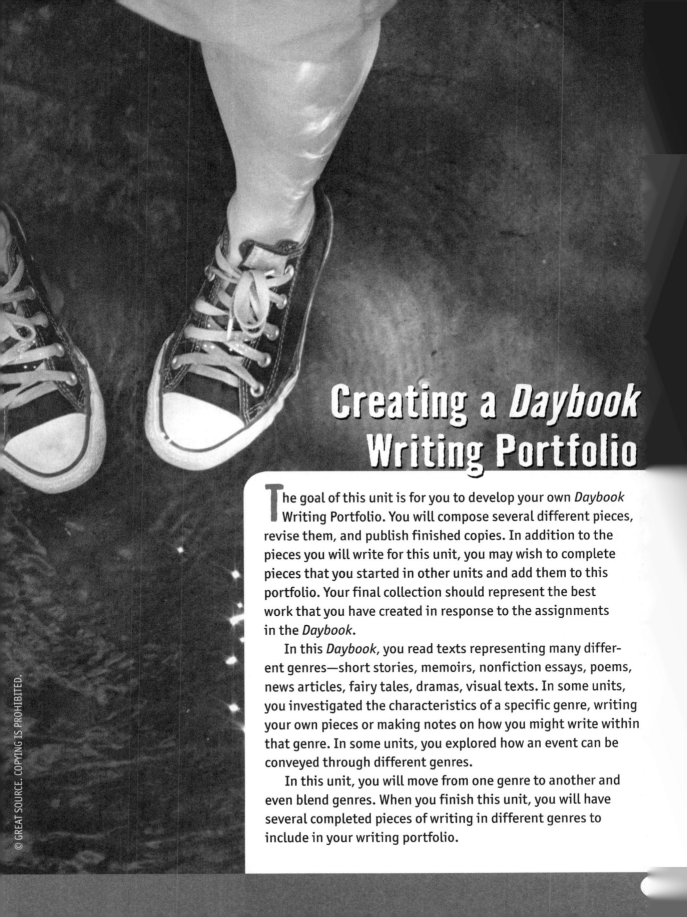

Creating a *Daybook* Writing Portfolio

The goal of this unit is for you to develop your own *Daybook* Writing Portfolio. You will compose several different pieces, revise them, and publish finished copies. In addition to the pieces you will write for this unit, you may wish to complete pieces that you started in other units and add them to this portfolio. Your final collection should represent the best work that you have created in response to the assignments in the *Daybook*.

In this *Daybook*, you read texts representing many different genres—short stories, memoirs, nonfiction essays, poems, news articles, fairy tales, dramas, visual texts. In some units, you investigated the characteristics of a specific genre, writing your own pieces or making notes on how you might write within that genre. In some units, you explored how an event can be conveyed through different genres.

In this unit, you will move from one genre to another and even blend genres. When you finish this unit, you will have several completed pieces of writing in different genres to include in your writing portfolio.

In this lesson, you will create a poem from a narrative using one of the three memoir pieces in Unit 3. Choose one of the three memoir selections and create a poem from selected words, phrases, or lines.

PROCESS

1 Choose one of the pieces and read it again, noticing phrases that are especially poetic.

2 Mark words, phrases, or lines that you think could be in a poem.

3 Write these words below, randomly.

_____

_____

_____

4 Look for a way to connect some or all of these words or phrases to make a new statement of your own.

5 Add words of your own as needed to make your poem flow.

Example: The poem that follows is based on words and phrases from *In Search of Our Mothers' Gardens* by Alice Walker. Words and phrases were highlighted in the excerpt, written in a list, and moved around. Some words were crossed off the list, but others were added. Notice the changes from *my* to *her* (first-person point of view changed to third-person). Notice also the added word *becomes* before the words *the earth*.

Inner Vision

Response Notes

A tree
is the last thing her right eye sees:
its trunk,
its branches
its leaves
blotted out by the rising blood.

The scar on her eye becomes
the earth as it appears from the moon,
bluish, full of light,
with whitish clouds swirling around it.

A world in her eye ❖

❄ Now sift through your collection of words to construct your own poem.
   Be sure to include a title.

_____

_____

_____

_____

_____

_____

_____

_____

_____

_____

_____

_____

_____

_____

_____

_____

_____

_____

_____

_____

_____

_____

_____

_____

❄ When you have finished, meet with a writing partner to test the
   effectiveness of your poem. Decide whether the images you chose
   communicate powerful ideas. Discuss how well the title goes with
   your poem. Help each other to make revisions that will
   strengthen your poems.

❄ Make a final copy of your poem for your portfolio when
   you have revised it to your satisfaction.

What kinds of
decisions does a poet
make when transforming
prose to poetry?

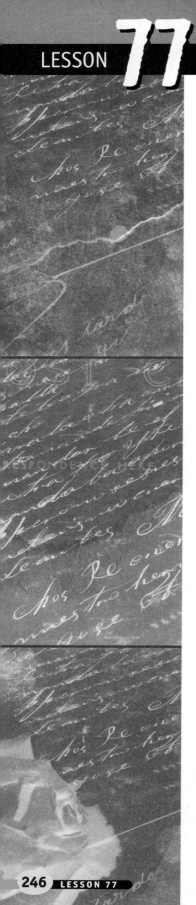

In the last lesson, you selected words from a memoir to construct a poem. In this lesson, you will read a poem and construct a story from it.

Reread the poem in Lesson 34 that Erin Keenan, a teenage poet in England, wrote after studying the story of Icarus. Of course, by definition, her poem already represents changed genres; it has its roots in the story we know from Ovid. As you reread the poem and your **Response Notes,** focus on the following elements:

- ■ Who is the speaker?

- ■ What are some situations that could have inspired this poem?

- ■ What is the setting? Include a possible place and time frame.

- ■ How would you describe Jen?

WRITING YOUR STORY

In the *Daybook*, you have studied the characteristics of short stories. To write your own story using this poem as a frame, expand your responses to the questions above. Remember that in this genre transformation from poem to story, you must stay true to the poem.

First, make some decisions about the two **characters** we know something about, the speaker and Jen. Remember, this is your story, so you can create any characters you want as long as you don't change what you know is in the poem.

✳ Describe the speaker. Some of the elements you must decide are these:
- ■ name
- ■ male or female
- ■ age and physical description
- ■ relationship to Jen
- ■ some definitive personality traits

✳ Describe Jen. Decide on these elements:
- ■ age and physical description
- ■ relationship to the speaker
- ■ some definitive personality traits

✳ The critical factor in this story is the situation. Select the situation you want to develop. What was the triggering event and what happened as a result?

■ *Triggering event* Be as precise as possible; give specifics.

_____

_____

_____

_____

■ *What happened as a result?* Again, be precise; use concrete imagery.

_____

_____

_____

_____

✳ You are now ready to write your story. Since stories are generally lengthy, use your own paper for your draft.

✳ When you have finished, work with a partner to examine several elements in each other's stories. Here are some starter questions:

■ Is the situation believable?

■ Do the events follow naturally from the triggering event?

■ Does the story reveal the relationship between the speaker and Jen?

■ Are there enough concrete details so that the reader can visualize what happens?

■ Is the story consistent with the poem?

■ How does your story relate to the original Icarus story?

✳ After you and your partner have discussed your story, revise it to make it more powerful. Then make a final copy for your portfolio.

What did you have to think about to transform poetry into prose?

GENRE CHANGE OF YOUR CHOICE

In Unit 4, you learned about autism from a number of different perspectives, each conveyed through a different genre. Reread the selections in Lessons 16, 17, 18, and 19. Choose any one of the three pieces—the novel excerpt, the scientific article, or the poem— and transform it into a different genre.

PROCESS

1 Decide which piece you will use as your source for information about autism.

My Source_____

2 Decide in which genre you are going to write—poem, story, essay, article, or play.

_____

3 Make notes about the elements you will consider as you write:

■ *Speaker* Will it be in your own voice or in another person's?

_____

_____

■ *Audience* Who might want to read it? Decide on a group of people or a specific person.

_____

_____

■ *Details* What are some of the details about autism that you plan to include?

_____   _____
_____   _____
_____   _____
_____   _____
_____   _____
_____   _____

WRITE YOUR DRAFT

✳ Write a draft of your piece here or on your own paper.

_____

_____

_____

_____

_____

_____

_____

_____

_____

_____

_____

_____

_____

_____

_____

_____

_____

_____

_____

_____

_____

✳ When you have finished writing your draft, meet with your writing partner to exchange drafts.

- ◼ Talk with each other about your intent in writing.
- ◼ Discuss the elements of the genre you selected.
- ◼ Read each other's writing from the perspective of how well it incorporates the characteristics of the genre.
- ◼ Make suggestions for revision.

✳ Once you have revised your writing to your satisfaction, make a clean copy for your portfolio.

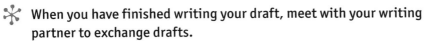
How do you decide which genre of writing is best suited to what you want to say?

CHARACTERISTICS OF TWO GENRES

In Unit 1 you read William Stafford's poem "Traveling through the Dark," about a situation that seemed, at first reading, to be similar to the situation in the newspaper article "Roadside Caesarean Saves a Fawn." As you worked through the unit, however, you saw that the two pieces were actually very different.

Reread both the newspaper feature and the poem in Unit 1 on pages 10 and 15. As you review these pieces, what can you say about the impact of the two different versions of a similar story? Does the difference in genre have an effect on the reader?

	Effect	Characteristics that create the effect
Newspaper story		
Poem		

TRANSFORMING A NEWSPAPER ARTICLE INTO A POEM

Find a newspaper article that elicits a strong response. Be sure the article has a strong story line. Highlight the basic elements of the story in the article to use in your poem. Change an aspect of the article to make a different kind of statement that is likely to elicit a different reader response. Use the space below to make notes.

Outline of the story in the paper:

_____

_____

_____

Some ways I might change the story for my poem:

_____

_____

_____

_____

_____

DRAFT OF MY POEM

_____

_____

_____

_____

_____

_____

_____

_____

_____

_____

_____

_____

_____

_____

_____

_____

_____

MAKING THE FINAL COPY
Meet with your writing partner to read your poems to each other.
Check to see whether you have used specific, concrete images to
get your idea across. Revise your poem to try to elicit a stronger
response. When you have revised the poem to your satisfaction,
make a final copy for your portfolio.

What are some
elements a poet might look
for when deciding what to
write about?

You know a lot about what makes one genre different from another. In this assignment, you will combine the elements of more than one genre in a reflective essay.

Make your knowledge about genres concrete. Select three different genres—poem, memoir, short story, myth, newspaper article, or scientific article—and write what you know about each one. Include one or two examples of each genre from the *Daybook*. Choose genres that you might consider blending.

Genres	Characteristics	Examples from the *Daybook*
1.		
2.		
3.		

BLENDING GENRES

The definition of one genre often blends into another genre. The two reflective essays in Unit 15 (Edward Abbey's "Freedom and Wilderness" and Annie Dillard's "Living Like Weasels") are examples of blended pieces. These two reflective essays are, in fact, a blend of memoir and reflection. There are reflective essays that do not have any elements of memoir; they are completely the author's thoughts on a subject. But when the author uses a personal experience as the basis for his or her ideas about a subject, then the piece becomes a blend.

WRITE A "BLENDED GENRE" REFLECTIVE ESSAY

Think about an incident in your life from which you gained an important insight about yourself, another person, or the way the world works.

 To gather your thoughts, ask yourself these questions:

- ■ What happened?
- ■ Where did it occur?
- ■ When did it occur?
- ■ What insight did you gain from this experience?

 Make notes on the incident here. Jot down details that are specific and make the reader part of your experience.

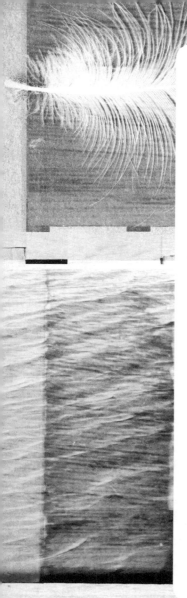

※ On your own paper, write the first draft of an essay about the experience. Once you have finished your draft, work with a writing partner to revise and strengthen your writing. As you read your partner's paper, look for clarity of insight into what the writer learned from the event. Use these questions as guidelines:

- Are the ideas clear and effective? Do the details support the main ideas?

- Are the ideas organized in a way that makes sense and has a strong impact on the reader?

- Does the writing have a unique voice?

- How effective is the word choice: are the nouns and verbs vivid and specific?

- Do the sentences flow when read aloud?

※ Edit the draft for correct grammar, usage, and mechanics. Finally, make a neat copy and add it to your portfolio.

SUMMING UP

※ As a final *Daybook* activity, gather the pieces you have written for this unit and arrange them into a portfolio.

- Make a cover for your portfolio which has a title, your name, class, and date.

- Make a table of contents that lists the title and the genre of each portfolio piece.

- On the final page, write a short reflection that evaluates the quality of your work as you progressed through the *Daybook*.

What have you learned from the *Daybook* about the genres you most like to read and write?

Becoming An Active Reader

Reading can entertain, inform, and reward. Reading also requires some hard work on the part of the reader. The sections that follow will help you get the most out of your reading.

The **reading process** section will guide you through reading a text. It will help you think about how to prepare to read (before reading), what to think about as you read (during reading), and how to get the most out of your reading by reflecting on it (after reading).

The **reading actively** section will show you how to interact with a text in order to get the most meaning out of it. It will show you how to engage with a text by using your brain and your pen—both at the same time!

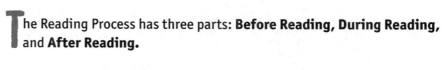

The Reading Process has three parts: **Before Reading, During Reading,** and **After Reading.**

1. BEFORE READING

✳ Preview the Material

Look over the selection before you read. Does the selection look like a short story or other work of fiction? If so, look at the title, introduction, and illustrations. Does the selection look like nonfiction? If so, look for headings, boldfaced words, photos, and captions. Also, ask yourself how the information is organized. Is the author comparing or contrasting information about the topic? Is the information presented in a sequence using signal words like first, second, third, and finally? Understanding how an author has organized information will help you to recognize key points as you read.

✳ Make Predictions

When you make predictions, you actively connect with the words on the page. Think about what you already know about the subject or the images. Then, think of yourself as a text detective, putting together what you know with new details in the text. Predict what you think will happen, why an event caused something to happen, or what might come next in a series of events.

✳ Set a Purpose

Begin by reviewing what you already know about the topic or situation in the text. Then, think about what you want to find out.

QUESTIONS TO ASK YOURSELF BEFORE READING

- Before I read this material, what do I think it is going to be about?
- After looking over the selection, what do I already know about this subject?
- What should I be thinking about as I read?

2. DURING READING

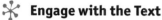

✳ Engage with the Text

As your eyes look at the words, your brain should be working to make connections between the words and what you already know. Have you had an experience similar to that of one of the characters in a story you are reading? Do you know someone like the character? Have you read another book about the topic? You will also want to connect what you read to the predictions you made before reading. *Confirm, revise, predict again* is a cycle that continues until you finish reading the material. All of these questions will go on inside your head. Sometimes, though, it helps to think out loud or write.

✳ Monitor Your Understanding

As you read, stop from time to time and ask yourself, "Do I understand what I just read?" If the text doesn't make sense, there are several steps that you can take.

- Go back and reread the text carefully.
- Read on to see if more information helps you understand.
- Pull together the author's ideas in a summary.
- Retell, or say in your own words, the events that have happened.
- Picture in your mind what the author described.
- Look for context clues or word-structure clues to help you figure out hard words.

This takes some practice. Remember, to be a successful reader, you must be an active reader. Make an effort to check your understanding every so often when you read a new selection.

QUESTIONS TO ASK YOURSELF WHILE YOU ARE READING

- What important details am I finding?
- Which of these ideas seem to be the most important?
- Does this information fit with anything I already know?
- What do I see in my mind as I read this material?
- Do I understand the information in the charts or tables? Does it help me to understand what I am reading?

3. AFTER READING

❋ Summarize
Reread to locate the most important ideas in the story or essay.

❋ Respond and Reflect
Talk with a partner about what you have read. What did you learn from the text? Were your predictions confirmed? What questions do you still have? Talking about reading helps you to better understand what you have read.

❋ Ask Questions
Try asking yourself questions that begin like this:

Can I compare or contrast . . .   *evaluate . . .*   *connect . . .*
                    examine . . .   *analyze . . .*   *relate . . .*

❋ Engage with the Text
Good readers engage with a text all the time, even when they have finished reading. When you tie events in your life or something else you have read to what you are currently reading or have read, you become more involved with your reading. In the process, you are learning more about your values, relationships in your family, and issues in the world around you.

QUESTIONS TO ASK YOURSELF AFTER READING
- What was this article about?
- What was the author trying to tell me?
- Have I learned something that made me change the way I think about this topic?
- Are there parts of this material that I really want to remember?

Make the effort to stay involved with your reading by reading actively. Your mind should be busy reading the text, making connections, making predictions, and asking questions. Your hand should be busy, too. Keep track of what you are thinking by "reading with your pen." **Write** your reactions to the text or connections that you can make. **Circle** words you don't understand. **Draw** a sketch of a scene. **Underline** or **highlight** an important idea. You may have your own way of reading actively. You may develop a style that works better for you, but here are six common ways of reading actively.

MARK OR HIGHLIGHT The most common way of noting important parts of a text is to write on a sticky note and put it on the page. Or, if you can, mark important parts of a text by highlighting them with a marker, pen, or pencil. You can also use highlighting tape. The highlighted parts should provide a good review of the text.

ASK QUESTIONS Asking questions is a way of engaging the author in conversation. Readers who ask a lot of questions think about the text more and understand it better. "Why is the writer talking about this?" "Is this really true?" "What does that mean?"

REACT AND CONNECT When you read, listen to the author and to yourself. Think about what you are reading and relate it to your own life. Compare and contrast what the text says to what you know.

PREDICT Readers who are involved with the text constantly wonder how things will turn out. They think about what might happen. They check their thoughts against the text and make adjustments. Sometimes the author surprises them! Making predictions helps you stay interested in what you are reading.

VISUALIZE Making pictures in your mind can help you "see"what you are thinking and help you remember. A chart, a sketch, a diagram—any of these can help you "see." Sometimes your picture doesn't match what you think the author is telling you. This is a signal to reread to check your understanding of the text.

CLARIFY As you read, you need to be sure that you understand what is going on in the text. Take time to pull together what you have learned. Try writing notes to clarify your understanding. Another way of checking to see that you understand is to tell someone about what you have read.

GLOSSARY

allusion an indirect reference

aside in a play, a character's speech directed at the audience only; a technique used to reveal the character's thoughts

attention to detail helps you fully understand and visualize what you read

audience the people whom the author intends to read his or her writing

build context interacting with a text by learning about the real life history and events that are part of the story

characterization the way an author reveals information about the people, animals, and imaginary creatures in a story

clarify to ask questions based on your reading that you did not know or confirm something you suspected but were not sure of

connections making a comparison between a text and your own life, or comparing a text and another text in order to deepen your understanding

connecting to the story being emotionally involved with the story

dialogue spoken words between two or more people

drama a written work that tells a story through action and dialogue

draw conclusions to come up with a summary of a situation based on information given

evaluating deciding on the value of something

evidence facts that support an argument

exploring multiple perspectives reading different points of view in order to think about a moment or event from more than one angle

extrapolation a technique in fantasy writing in which the writer includes some detail or information from reality to help the reader connect with the story

fairy tale a fictional tale of legendary deeds and creatures

fantasy a type of fiction featuring imaginary worlds and magical or supernatural events

first-person point of view the telling of a story in which the narration is one of the characters and calls himself or herself "I"

focus on language and craft a reading strategy that involves paying attention to the author's word choice as well as how the author uses words to evoke a response

folktale a story or legend that is part of an oral tradition

frame and focus how a filmmaker sets a scene

genre a type of writing

graphic novel a story presented as a cartoon

iambic pentameter a poetic construction that uses a series of five pairs of syllables in which the first is unstressed and the second is stressed

image a mental picture created by a reader as he or she reads

infer to make an inference

inferences reasonable guesses you make by putting together something you have read with something you already know

interacting with the text "carrying on a conversation" with a text: a strategy for effective reading that involves circling, underlining, and writing notes

making connections a reading strategy that involves comparing a text to your memories or to another text in order to deepen your understanding

memoir a writer's written reflection on his or her earlier life

metaphor an indirect comparison that implies a similarity between two things that are not similar

method of inquiry using the five essential strategies to investigate a text

modeling a poem using the structure of a poem as a foundation to write a new poem

myth a traditional story that is representative of the culture it originated from

narrative strategies characteristics of a story, such as characters, dialogue, and setting

nonfiction factual writing

objective without emotion or bias

personal narrative a short prose piece in which a writer expresses personal thoughts and makes connections

perspective the point of view or angle from which a subject is seen

persuasion an attempt to convince others to feel the same way you do

plot how the characters and events in a story are connected

point of view the perspective from which a story is told

prediction an educated guess about upcoming events that is based on background knowledge and clues from the text

protagonist the main character in a piece of writing

purpose an author's intent in writing

read with your pen a method of tracking of your interaction with a text by circling, underlining, or writing notes

reconstruct to build again

reflective essay an essay in which the writer expresses his or her thoughts about a subject and invites the reader to do so as well

repetition the repeating of a word or phrase to emphasize a point

retelling a new version of an original story in which the time frame has been changed to reflect modern values

revision looking at a draft again in order to find ways to improve it

rhymed couplet two lines of poetry in a row that rhyme at the end

simile a direct comparison of two things that are different; the words *like* and *as* are used in most similes

science fiction a written work that deals with the influence of real or imagined science on society or on individuals

sonnet a fourteen line poem that begins with an idea, question, or challenge to be resolved

speaker tags in a play, the feature that identifies which character is speaking

story board a series of panels that show rough sketches of key scenes

strategy a carefully designed plan of action for reaching a goal

structure the way a piece of writing is put together, the arrangement of its words, sentences, paragraphs, chapters, and so on

studying an author a reading strategy that involves inquiring into an author's life experiences and perspective to inform the meaning that you find in reading a text

style a writer's unique way of writing as shown by the decisions the writer typically makes as to sentence length, description, figurative language, and tone

subjective reflecting the writers thoughts; personal

supporting evidence facts, statistics, examples, observations, quotations, and experts' opinions that support and argument

symbol an image or object that represents other things

synthesizing the strategies to apply the knowledge you gain from reading and writing about a topic to better your understanding of that topic

thesis statement the main topic or message that is explored through the characters and plot of a story

tone the attitude a writer takes toward a subject or character

verbal snapshot a written description of a place or moment in time

visual text a collection of visual images that present a coherent message

visualizing a reading strategy in which a reader makes pictures of a text in his or her mind

voice the narration style of an author

working definition the definition you assign to an unfamiliar word in a text until you look in a dictionary

10 "Roadside Caesarean Saves a Fawn" by Chris Smith. ©The Press Democrat, Santa Rosa, CA.

15 "Traveling through the Dark" Copyright 1962, 1998 by the Estate of William Stafford. Reprinted from *The Way It Is: New & Selected Poems* with the permission of Graywolf Press, Saint Paul, Minnesota.

22 From *Writing the Australian Crawl* by William Stafford, University of Michigan Press.

23 Excerpt from a letter written by William Stafford to Ted Kooser. Used by permission of the author.

26 Reprinted from *The Light on the Tent Wall: A Bridging*, by permission of the American Indian Studies Center, UCLA, © 1990 Regents of the University of California.

28 Excerpt from *Brave Men* by Ernie Pyle. Used by permission of Scripps Howard Foundation.

34 Li-Young Lee's "Mnemonic" from *Rose*. Copyright © 1986 by Li-Young Lee. Reprinted with the permission of BOA Editions, Ltd., www.BOAEditions.org. (world rights except UK) Li-Young Lee, *From Blossoms: Selected Poems* (Bloodaxe Books, 2007) www.bloodaxebooks.com. (UK rights)

40 Excerpt from pp. 35–6 from *Paula* by Isabel Allende and trans. by Margaret Sayers Peden. Copyright © 1994 by Isabel Allende. Translation copyright © 1995 by HarperCollins Publishers. Reprinted by permission of HarperCollins Publishers.

43 Excerpt from pp. 19–21 from *Dust Tracks* on a Road by Zora Neale Hurston. Copyright © 1942 by Zora Neale Hurston; renewed © 1970 by John C. Hurston. Reprinted by permission of HarperCollins Publishers.

46 From *Black White and Jewish* by Rebecca Walker, copyright © 2001 by Rebecca Walker. Used by permission of Riverhead Books, an imprint of Penguin Group (USA) Inc.

49 From *In Search of Our Mother's Gardens* by Alice Walker. Copyright ©1983 by Alice Walker. Used by permission of Harcourt Brace.

56, 60 From THE CURIOUS INCIDENT OF THE DOG IN THE NIGHT-TIME by Mark Haddon, copyright © 2003 by Mark Haddon. Used by permission of Doubleday, a division of Random House, Inc.

63 From "Understanding Autism" by Geoffrey Cowley, Donna Foote, and Heather Won Tesoriero et al. Originally published in Newsweek, 136.5, July 31, 200, used by permission.

66 "Autism Poem: The Grid" by Barbara Crooker.

Appears in her book *Radiance*, World Press, 2005. Used by permission of the author.

68 "Autism" by Brett Shaw. Used by permission.

72 "Twenty Questions" from *Collected Poems* by Donald Justice, copyright © 2004 by Donald Justice. Used by permission of Alfred A. Knopf, a division of Random House, Inc.

75, 76, 78, 79 Pablo Neruda, excerpts from *The Book of Questions*, translated by William O'Daly. Copyright © 1974 by Pablo Neruda and the Heirs of Pable Neruda. Translation copyright ©1991, 2001 by William O'Daly. Reprinted by permission of Copper Canyon Press, www.coppercanyonpress.org.

81 "Some Questions You Might Ask" from *House of Light* by Mary Oliver. Copyright © 1990 by Mary Oliver. Reprinted by permission of Beacon Press.

83 "What Is It?" from *House of Light* by Mary Oliver. Copyright © 1990 by Mary Oliver. Reprinted by permission of Beacon Press, Boston.

88 Excerpt from "The Eye of the Heron" by Ursula K. Le Guin. Copyright © 1978 by Ursula K. Le Guin; first appeared in *Millennial Women*. Reprinted by permission of the author, and the author's agent, Virginia Kidd.

91 Excerpt from "The Kerastion" by Ursula K. Le Guin. Copyright © 1990 by Ursula K. Le Guin; first appeared in the *Westercon 1990 Program Book*. Reprinted by permission of the author, and the author's agent Virginia Kidd.

94 Excerpt from "Darkness Box" by Ursula K. Le Guin. © 1963, Copyright © 1990, 1991 by Ursula K. Le Guin; first appeared in the *Westercon 1990 Program Book*. Reprinted with permission of the author, and the author's agent Virginia Kidd.

99 From *Dancing at the Edge of the World* by Ursula Le Guin. Copyright © 1989 by Ursula K. Le Guin. Used by permission of Grove/Atlantic, Inc.

102 "Before the Fall" by Harriet Archer, used by permission of the author, Harriet Archer.

106 "Ghost" By Peter McDonald. Used by permission.

106 "Icarus" by Lyman Andrews. Used by permission of the author.

109 "Icarus" by Edward Field. By permission of the author.

111 "Jennifer and Icarus" by Erin Pearl Keenan. Used by permission of Erin Pearl Keenan.

112 "Icarus, Come with Me" by Bill Whiteman. Used by permission.

114 "Musée des Beaux Arts" by W.H. Auden. Copyright © 1940 by W.H. Auden. Reprinted by permission of Curtis Brown, Ltd.

119 "The People Could Fly: American Black Folktales" by Virginia Hamilton, used by permission of Random House Inc.

120 "Ebos Landing," used by permission of *New Georgia Encyclopedia*, http://georgiaencyclopedia.org.

122 "All God's Chillen Had Wings" from *The Book of Negro Folklore*, edited by Langston Hughes and Arna Bontemps.

126 From *Black Ice* by Lorene Cary, copyright © 1991 by Lorene Cary. Used by permission of Alfred A. Knopf, a division of Random House, Inc.

128 "O Daedalus, Fly Away Home." Copyright © 1966 by Robert Hayden, from *Collected Poems of Robert Hayden* by Robert Hayden, edited by Frederick Glaysher. Used by permission of Liveright Publishing Company.

130 "Frederick Douglass." Copyright © 1966 by Robert Hayden, from *Collected Poems of Robert Hayden* by Robert Hayden, edited by Frederick Glaysher. Used by permission of Liveright Publishing Company.

131 From "Introduction" by Arnold Rampersad from *Collected Poems of Robert Hayden* . Used by permission of Arnold Rampersad.

134, 138, 140 "The Veil," and "The Bicycle" from *Persepolis*, by Marjane Satrapi, translation by L'Association. Copyright © 2003. Used by permission of Pantheon Books.

142 Excerpted from "Islamic Revolution of Iran," Microsoft® Encarta® Online Encyclopedia 2007, http://encarta.msn.com © 1997–2007 Microsoft Corporation. All rights reserved.

145 Excerpt from "On Writing *Persepolis*" by Marjane Satrapi. Used by permission of Random House Inc.

151 Excerpt from *Little Red and the Big Bad* by Will Shetterly. Used by permission of the author.

153 From *Lon Po Po* by Ed Young, copyright © 1989 by Ed Young. Used by permission of Philomel Books, A Division of Penguin Young Readers Group, A Member of Penguin Group (USA) Inc., 345 Hudson Street, New York, NY 10014. All rights reserved.

156 "Lupe" copyright © 2003 by Kathe Koja. Published by permission of Kathe Koja c/o Ralph M. Vicinanza Ltd.

159 "The Seven Stage a Comeback." Copyright © 2000 Gregory Maguire. Reprinted by permission of John Hawkins & Associates, Inc.

162 Reprinted with the permission of Simon & Schuster Books for Young Readers, an imprint of Simon & Schuster Children's Publishing Division from *Swan Sister* edited by Ellen Datlow and Terri Windling. Introduction copyright © 2003 Terri Windling.

166 Copyright 2005 by the National Association of School Psychologists, Bethesda, MD. Adapted by permission of the publisher.

169, 171 From *Always Running-La Vida Loca, Gang Days in L.A.* by Luis J. Rodriguez (Curbstone Press, 1993) Reprinted with permission of Curbstone Press. Distributed by Consortium.

173 "Race Politics," by Luis J. Rodriguez, from *Poems Across the Pavement*. Copyright © 1989 by Tia Chucha Press. Reprinted by permission.

182 "Did I Miss Anything?" by Tom Wayman. Used by permission of Harbour Publishing.

185 "Digging for China" from *Things of this World*, copyright © 1956 and renewed 1984 by Richard Wilbur, reprinted by permission of Harcourt, Inc. This material may not be reproduced in any form or by any means without the prior written permission of the publisher.

188, 189 "Even" and "The Lives of Rain" from The *Lives of Rain*, published by Interlink Books, an imprint of Interlink Publishing Group, Inc. Text copyright © Nathalie Handal, 2005. Reprinted by permission.

191 "Marshall" by George Macbeth. Used by permission of Sheil Land Associates, Ltd.

194 "My Father After Work" by Gary Gildner from *Blue Like the Heavens: New and Selected Poems*. Copyright © 1984. Reprinted by permission of the University of Pittsburgh Press.

196 Naomi Shihab Nye, "The Rider" from *Fuel*. Copyright © 1998 by Naomi Shihab Nye. Reprinted with the permission of BOA Editions, Ltd., www.boaeditions.org.

198 "The Words under the Words" from *19 Varieties of Gazelle: Poems of the Middle East* by Naomi Shihab Nye. Copyright © 2002 Naomi Shihab Nye. Used by permission of HarperCollins Publishers.

201 "Blood" from *19 Varieties of Gazelle: Poems of the Middle East* by Naomi Shihab Nye. Copyright © 2002 Naomi Shihab Nye. Used by permission of HarperCollins Publishers.

203 "The Orange, the Fig, the Whisper of Grapes" by Naomi Shihab Nye. Used by permission of the author, 2007.

209 Excerpt from "Skin, Our Largest Organ, Presents

and Protects Us" by Suguru Imaeda, MD from *Yale Health Care* March/April 2000.

209 "Two Countries" from *19 Varieties of Gazelle: Poems of the Middle East* by Naomi Shihab Nye. Copyright © 2002 Naomi Shihab Nye. Used by permission of HarperCollins Publishers.

212, 216, 220, 224, 227 "War of the Words," by Robin F. Brancato, © 1990, as published in *Center Stage: One-Act Plays for Teenage Readers and Actors* ed. by Donald R. Gallo, Harper and Row Publishers.

230 "Freedom and Wilderness, Wilderness and Freedom" from *The Journey Home* by Edward Abbey, copyright © 1977 by Edward Abbey. Used by permissions of Dutton, a division of Penguin Group (USA) Inc.

235, 239 "Living Like Weasels" excerpt (422–426) from *Teaching a Stone to Talk* by Annie Dillard. Copyright © 1982 by Annie Dillard. Used by permission of HarperCollins Publishers, Inc.

ILLUSTRATIONS

134 *b*, 135, 136 *t*, 138, 139 *l*, 140 *b*, 141 *t*: Marjane Satrapi.

PHOTOGRAPHY

Photo Research by AARTPACK, Inc.

Cover: © Grant Faint/Getty Images; **3–8:** © Hannu Liivaar/Fotolia.

Unit 1 9: © William Whitehurst/Corbis; **10:** © Thinkstock/Corbis; **11 *t*:** © Radiusimages/Inmagine; **11 *b*:** © Thinkstock/Corbis; **12:** © Radiusimages/Inmagine; **13, 14:** © MedioImages/Corbis; **15:** © Image100/Corbis; **16:** © Designpics/Inmagine; **17, 18, 19:** © Image100/Inmagine; **20, 21:** © James Thornton/Getty Images; **22, 23:** © MedioImages/Getty Images; **24:** © Designpics/Inmagine.

Unit 2 25: © Robert Michael/Corbis; **26:** © Image100/Corbis; **27:** © DLILLC/Corbis; **28:** © Sea World of California/Corbis; **29:** © Corbis; **30:** © Sea World of California/Corbis; **31, 32, 33:** © Philippe Colombi/Getty Images; **34:** © Johner RF/Getty Images; **35:** © Ingram/Inmagine; **36, 37:** © Photodisc/Getty Images; **38:** © Image100/Corbis.

Unit 3 39: © Bryan Mullennix/Getty Images; **40:** © Liane Cary/Veer; **41, 42:** © Mel Curtis/Getty Images; **43:** © DAJ/Getty Images; **44, 45:** © John Rich; **46:** © Bettmann/CORBIS; **47:** © Lorelyn Medina/Fotolia; **48:** © Inspirestock/Inmagine; **49 *t*:** © Jules Frazier/Getty Image; **49 *b*:** © Image Source/Corbis; **50 *t*:** © Jules Frazier/Getty Image; **50 *b*:** © Image Source/Corbis; **51:** © Skip Nall/Getty Images; **52:** © Javier Pierini/Getty Images; **53:** © Skip Nall/Getty Images; **54:** © Javier Pierini/Getty Images.

Unit 4 55: © Hill Street Studios/BlendImages/Corbis; **56 *t*:** © Image100/Corbis; **56 *b*:** © James P Blair/Getty Images; **57:** © Mike Watson Images/Corbis; **58:** © Image100 /Corbis; **59:** © Isabelle Rozenbaum/Getty Images; **60:** © Headhunters/Getty Images; **61:** © Photodisc/Inmagine; **62:** © Isabelle Rozenbaum/Getty Images; **63:** © John FoxxGetty Images; **64, 65:** © Carson Ganci/Design Pics/Corbis; **66 *t*:** © Megumi Takamura/Getty Images; **66b, 67:** © Sami Sarkis/Getty Images; **68:** © Ablestock/Inmagine; **69, 70:** © Jose Luis Pelaez Inc/Blend Images/Corbis.

Unit 5 71: ©Barry/Hulton Archive/Getty Images; **72 *t*:** © Lawrence Manning/Corbis; **72 *b*:** ©Heather Cachat/Fotolia; **73, 74:** © Akira Kaede/PhotoDisc/Getty Images; **75:** © Condé Nast Archive/Corbis; **76:** © Don Farrall/Getty Images; **77:** © Morey Milbradt/Brand X/Corbis; **78 *t*:** © Ron Chapple/Getty Images; **78 *b*, 79:** © Danilo Calilung/Corbis; **80:** © George Marks/Getty Images; **81 *t*:** © PhotoLink/Getty Images; **81 *b*, 82:** ©2004 Comstock Images, LLC; **83:** © Bryan Mullennix/Getty Images; **84, 85:** © Goodshoot/Corbis; **86:** © Morey Milbradt/Brand X/Corbis.

Unit 6 87: ©Robert Liewellyn/Corbis; **88:** © Luc Durocher/Fotolia; **89:** © Brandxpictures/Inmagine; **90:** © Robert Liewellyn/Corbis; **91, 92:** © Jack Hollingsworgh/Getty Images; **93:** © Digitalvision/Inmagine; **94:** © MedioImages/Corbis; **95, 96:** © JupiterImages; **97, 98:** © Patrick Koslo/Brand X/Corbis; **99:** © Julian Winslow/Corbis; **100:** © Fotosearch.

Unit 7 101: ©Josef Fankhauser/Getty Images; **102:** © Stockbyte/Getty Images; **103:** © John Foxx/Getty Images; **104:** © Photolink/PhotoDisc/Getty Images; **105:** © Rene Frederick/Getty Images; **106:** Photolink/PhotoDisc/Getty Images; **108:** © Stockbyte/Getty Images; **109:** © John Foxx/Getty Images; **110:** © Mats Widen/Getty Images; **111, 112:** © Sami Sarkis/Getty Images; **113:** © Natural Selection David Ponton/Design Pics/Corbis; **114 *l*:** © Rene Frederick/Getty Images; **114 *c*:** © Peter the Elder Brueghel/The Bridgeman Art Library/Getty Images; **115:** © Sami Sarkis/Getty Images;

116: © Rene Frederick/Getty Images.

Unit 8 117: © Carl Iwasaki/Getty Images;
118, 119: © Michael Aw/Getty Images;
120, 121: © Image Source/Corbis; **122:** © Mimotito/
Getty Images; **123, 124:** © Deborah Jaffe/Getty
Images; **125:** © Emanuele Taroni/Getty Images;
126 l: © Jupiterimages/Brand X/Corbis;
126 b: © Marco Antonio Fernández/Fotolia;
127: © John Foxx/Getty Images; **128:** © Emanuele
Taroni/Getty Images; **129:** © John Foxx/Getty
Images; **130:** © Photodisc/Getty Images;
131: © Pach Brothers/Corbis; **132:** © Emanuele
Taroni/Getty Images.

Unit 9 133: © CORBIS; **134 t:** © Jean Guichard/
Sygma/CORBIS; **136 b:** © DAJ/Getty Images;
137: © Cory Langley/Corbis; **139 r:** © Alain Keler/
Sygma/Corbis; **140t, 141r, 142:** © DAJ/Getty
Images; **143:** © Diego Goldberg/Sygma/Corbis;
144: © Patrick Chauvel/Sygma/Corbis;
145, 146: © DAJ/Getty Images; **147, 148:** © Cory
Langley/Corbis.

Unit 10 149: © Kamil Vojnar/Getty Images;
150: © Photodisc/Getty Images; **151 t:** © Jeffrey Van
Daele/Fotolia; **151b:** © Spike Mafford/Getty Images;
152: © Photodisc/Getty Images; **153:** © Tom Brake-
field/Getty Images; **154:** © Philip Harvey/Corbis;
155: © Kaz Chiba/PhotoDisc/Getty Images;
156: © Darrell Gulin/Getty Images; **157:** © Think-
stock/Corbis; **158:** © Darrell Gulin/Getty Images;
159, 160: © Rosemary Calvert/Getty Images;
161: © Michael S. Yamashita/CORBIS; **162:** © Image
Source Pink/Getty Images; **163, 164:** © Spike Maf-
ford/Getty Images.

Unit 11 165: ©Fox Photos/Getty Images;
166: © ImageShop/Corbis; **167:** © Image Source
Pink/Getty Images; **168:** © Image100/Corbis;
169: © Sami Sarkis/Getty Images; **170:** © Image100/
Corbis; **171:** © Sami Sarkis/Getty Images;
172: © Image**100**/Corbis; **173, 174:** © George Marks/
Getty Images; **175, 176:** © Robert Landau/Corbis;
177, 178: © George Marks/Getty Images.

Unit 12 179: © Pixland/Corbis; **180:** © Ryan Mc-
Vay/Getty Images; **181, 182:** © Tom Merton/Getty
Images; **183 t:** © Hazel Proudlove/Fotolia;
183 b: © Image Source/Corbis; **184, 185:** © Jo-
seph Sohm/Visions of America/Corbis; **186 t:** ©
Hanson Ng/Design Pics/Corbis; **186 b:** © Joseph

Sohm/Visions of America/Corbis; **187, 188:** © Steve
Bowman/Corbis; **189:** © Image Source/Corbis;
190, 191: © Sue Wilson/Getty Images; **192:** ©
limeyrunner/Fotolia; **193:** © Doug Menuez/Getty Images; **194:** © Andersen Ross/Getty Images.

Unit 13 195: © James Evans/Stephen Barclay
Agency; **196 t:** © Gina Minielli/Corbis;
196 b: © Harutaka Nodera/MIXA/Getty Images;
197: © Harutaka Nodera/MIXA/Getty Images;
198: © John A Rizzo/Getty Images; **199, 200:** © Don
Farrall/Getty Images; **201 t:** © foodstylist/Fotolia;
201 b, 202: © Digital Vision/Getty Images;
203 t: © Thinkstock/Corbis; **203 b:** © foodstylist/
Fotolia; **204:** © Loredana/Fotolia;
205, 206: © Thinkstock/Corbis; **207, 208:** © Paul
Edmondson/PhotoDisc/Getty Images;
209t: © Tanya Constantine/Getty Images;
209 b: © © Paul Edmondson/PhotoDisc/Getty
Images; **210:** © Tanya Constantine/Getty Images.

Unit 14 211: © Alinari Archives/Corbis; **212:** © Jack
Hollingsworth/Corbis; **213, 214:** JupiterImages;
215: © Mike Kemp/Getty Images;
216, 217, 218: © Image100/Corbis; **219:** © Rayman/
Getty Images; **220:** © George Doyle/Getty Images;
221, 222: © Medioimages/Photodisc/Getty Images;
223: JupiterImages; **224, 225:** © Image100/Corbis;
226: © Don Farrall/Getty Images;
227: © Bloomimage/Corbis; **228:** © Don Farrall/
Getty Images.

Unit 15 229: © Morgan David de Lossy/Corbis;
230: © Jason Edwards/Getty Images; **231:** © Good-
shoot/Corbis; **232:** © Jason Edwards/Getty Images;
233, 234: © Goodshoot/Corbis; **235:** © Mike Watson
Images/Corbis; **236:** © Bruce Heinemann/Photo-
Disc/Getty Images; **237, 238:** © Tom Brakefield/Getty
Images; **239:** © Mike Watson Images/Corbis;
240: © Image100/Corbis; **241:** © Don Farrall/Getty
Images; **242:** © Image100/Corbis.

Unit 16 243: © Karen Zukowski/Corbis;
244, 245: © Karl Weatherly/Getty Images;
246, 247: © Roxana Gonzalez/Fotolia;
248, 249: © JupiterImages; **250, 251:** © Digital
Vision/Getty Images; **252, 253, 254:** © Nanette
Hooslag/Getty Images.

Becoming an Active Reader 255: © Roy McMahon/
Corbis; **256, 257, 258:** © Kasia75/Fotolia;
259: © Knauer/Johnson/JupiterImages.